Where Ki... Grew

STORIES FROM A
WESTCOUNTRY CHILDHOOD

Lewis Wilshire

Broadcast
B O O K S

B R I S T O L

This book is dedicated to BBC Radio Bristol in general, and in particular to Pete Lawrence, who made the stories come alive, and also to my daughter Hilary, to Trevor Fry and David Harrison

Contents

Where Kingcups Grew

First published in England in 2002
by
Broadcast Books,
4 Cotham Vale,
Bristol,
BS6 6HR,
Tel 0117 973 2010
www.broadcastbooks.co.uk

Several of the stories in this collection have been previously
broadcast by Trevor Fry for BBC Radio Bristol,
read by Pete Lawrence.

Design by **Martin St Amant**

Cover painting by **Kit Edward**

Drawings and engravings by **Jenny Ibrahim**

Photographs from the author's collection

Printed in Great Britain by
The Bath Press,
Lower Bristol Road,
Bath.

ISBN 1-874092-81-8

*Several stories from this book are also available on audio
cassette, from Broadcast Books, read by Pete Lawrence.*

Foreword

I *first became aware of Lewis Wilshire years ago through the mutual links between him and my father as members of the British Association of Industrial Editors. Our paths next crossed when I was a reporter on the **Evening Post** and he was press contact at Courage's flourishing brewery in Bath Street. Finally we bumped into each other once more as Courage withdrew from Bristol and Lewis was reborn as a superb chronicler of his South Gloucestershire childhood in a series of tales I had been printing in the **Bristol Times**. And from those stories, I am delighted to say, arose the idea for this book.*

*Yet all this time, and to my shame, I had no idea of the other Lewis Wilshire—the writer, the novelist, the sharer of Liquorice Allsorts with John Betjeman, the colleague of T S Eliot and reluctant drinking companion of Dylan Thomas. To begin with, there were the articles dating back to the war for the **Bristol Observer**, **Woman's Own** and **The Evening Post**. Some of the stories were translated into German (I hope they didn't try to capture the elusive South Gloucestershire dialect he uses in his childhood tales) which resulted in a visit from the police investigating suspicions of Nazi sympathies. Then there* were the West Country village life novels—News **from the Hamlet** (1949), **Spring Song** (1951) and **Summer of Enchantment** (1952), which were greatly admired by his old friend John Betjeman. The stream of novels stopped abruptly after a row with publishers Dent who rejected an anti-war novel he'd submitted after **Spring Song** as being out of keeping with the spirit of the times. However they still needed something in the familiar Wilshire style because it was promised in their autumn books catalogue. Lewis wrote them **Summer of Enchantment** in a six week fury and then abandoned novel writing completely.

But perhaps his most memorable creation is a book I have long treasured—published in 1954 and reissued in 1980—**Berkeley Vale and Severn Shore**. The rather uninspiring title—firmly of its time— belies the humanity, clarity and perspicacity of the prose. Lewis set out to walk the length of the Severn, talking with old craftsmen, farmers, landowners, salmon netters—anyone who lived and worked on Severnside when it was still a rural valley with no intrusive motorways or road bridges. As a portrait of an area and its inhabitants, it remains a landmark for its perception and insights.

These were the days when Lewis' work as a Public Information Officer for Courage gave him the opportunity to create another record of West Country life, in the form of a vast photographic archive of the inns and pubs in the region, many now vanished. To Lewis' surprise and pleasure, this unique collection is currently being catalogued by real ale campaigners CAMRA as **The Lewis Wilshire Collection**.

Lewis suffered a stroke in 1990 which sadly brought an end to his writing days, although his stories still reach a wide audience of admirers through their continued run in the **Bristol Times** and broadcasts on BBC Radio Bristol. **Where Kingcups Grew** is Lewis's own selection of these favorites, the crowning of a long career as a superb story teller and chronicler of almost forgotten times.

David Harrison, November 2002

Agnes

SHE LOOKED LIKE A SPINSTER, she talked like a spinster and everybody assumed she would stay a spinster. When I was a boy she was thirty-odd, a teacher down Sunday school, forewoman in the boot factory and mainstay of the home. Her mother had died twenty years before, leaving her the responsibilities of a demanding, old-fashioned father and a home full of elaborate china ornaments...

Gran herself was a great collector of ornaments but our house couldn't compare with the Whitlows', either for the quantity or complexity of its china junk. No other house in the hamlet could boast so many sepia photographs of the dear-departed, so many religious tracts or presents from Weymouth or Weston-super-Mare. Yet, with it all, the Whitlow place was always as clean as a new pin.

Every day Agnes washed and polished each individual monstrosity with delicate, loving care. Great-uncles and aunts who had long since shuffled off their mortal coils were kept alive in their photographs, and tracts which reminded the casual visitor and family alike of the need to repent before it was too late never attracted the merest wisp of cobweb. To Agnes, her parents' home was a shrine, she its priestess. Her father, a joyless old man who had never given up mourning his previous slave, her mother, seemed to resent bitterly that he had never incurred any sins to repent of and bleated for attention, regularly, like an ancient sheep.

She'll never change, everybody said, a spinster if there ever was one, dry as a bit of stick.

Mind, she wasn't unattractive. Looking back, she had a sort of elusive, vulnerable beauty. Her face was too square but she had a slim figure without being skinny and every part of her moved. Unlike most spinsters she never seemed to be stiff, never dispirited, quick to respond to others, always neat and tidy, decent without being smart.

So, when the whispers started, nobody believed them. "Impossible," they said, "out of the question"—whilst they thought "But how exciting if it *were* true". And they went on, increased, until they began to take hold.

My Gran was adamant from the first.

"I won't believe it," she said, "and nobody can make me. After all," peering wisely over her glasses as she went on with her stitching "I ought to know. I makes every stitch she's got on."

That was true. She did. Because she was the local dressmaker, Gran had an unparalleled knowledge of female bodies. She didn't need to measure them unless they had put on weight or lost it. She knew them down to the last inch. And this intimate knowledge of their shape and flesh gave her an extraordinary insight into their personality.

"I can tell by the way they holds theirselves" she'd say, quietly, to a chosen friend. "I'd take my oath on it, Sal, she's never been touched."

Gran was usually right. She had a sort of extra-sense which communicated with their inner-being via a tape measure and fingertips, and it was helped by her knowledge of human nature. Gran herself was plump, serene and happy in her work. She loved making pretty dresses, participating in gossip, and she was an ardent reader of tuppenny romances. I used to sit there and watch her stitching away in the lamplight and it seemed to me she had found the secret of happiness that eluded the rest of us. Gran had never doubted that God was in His heaven and that, no matter what we think, All is for the Best.

Because she always seemed so sure, I tended to see people—or, more especially, women, very much as Gran saw them, I had reservations about her extra-sensory perception when it came to men. Without that tactile contact of dressmaking, Gran seemed to me to be weak in her judgment of men. After all, if she'd been any sort of judge she would never have married Granfer, who was grumpy, mean, tyrannical and narrow-minded…

As I say, Gran loved a gossip, and some people said our cottage was a clearing-house for it but, all the same, when Milly Cook came in with that tale about seeing Aggie with a man, Gran lost her temper for once.

"Why can't 'ee leave her alone, poor soul?" she said "We all know it can't be true. The truth is, she ain't got it in her."

"I'm only saying what I saw with me own two eyes, Mrs Wilshire."

Putting aside the skirt she was working on Gran looked at her severely.

"You *thought* you saw her, Milly. It must've been someone else. You said yourself it was dark."

"It wasn't all *that* dark, Mrs Wilshire, and I felt sure… and then there was that dress…"

"Dress? What dress?"

"Her green one, he with the leaves on."

This was more serious than previous stories. After all, a face in a dark lane can be mistaken for another face but a dress is a dress.

"I can swear to that green dress," Milly said excitedly. "I

specially noticed the belt with the big button."

Gran knew that belt. She had bought the button and sewn it on herself.

"Milly Cook," she said, "we've been friends for more years than I can remember but if you breathe a word—a single word—about that dress, I'll never... speak to 'ee again."

With tears in her eyes Milly promised, and after she was gone Gran was strangely silent.

"Do you think she was right, Gran?" I asked.

"You read your book and bide quiet!"

That, too, was unlike her. She loved to talk about her customers, knowing that secrets were safe with me. It was like talking to herself.

A week later Agnes herself came for a fitting. Gran was alone (I was there but then I didn't count). She seemed the same as ever. They both did until Gran told her to take her coat off.

Did I tell you Gran had a particular way of looking at female bodies, sizing them up; not seeing the body as Sal or Milly or Agnes but as a personality in itself? I could tell straight away there was something up. Gran reddened round the neck and her voice went odd "You'm puttin' on a bit of weight, Aggie, yes, quite a bit."

Agnes became flustered at this.

She laughed. "Middle-aged spread, I s'pose."

"I don't think so, my dear. It's in the wrong place."

Agnes looked at her and blushed deeply. Started to cry. Turning to me, Gran said, quite sharply, "Go and see your Granfer."

"But he'll be asleep on the sofa and you know what he..."

I never finished the sentence because Gran looked at me and nodded toward the door. There was no need for her to be more explicit. I went.

This is a story I can't finish because I don't know what happened or how it ended. It was all very unsatisfactory. Gran never told me what made Aggie cry. Old Mr Whitlow went to live with his sister up at Hanham and Agnes disappeared, went to stay with a relative up North. She never came back and although people tried to find out from Gran what was behind it all, she never told the truth. Not even to me.

My Gran, standing outside her cottage

Gran's friend Deborah who taught her the art of decoration with Jet—possibly wearing one of the dresses that Gran made for her

Uncle Tom

I SHALL ALWAYS BE GRATEFUL for having such a rich and varied collection of aunts and uncles. It seemed to me, when I was a kid, that I had a bigger ration than other boys I knew. Of course I didn't appreciate them—well, one doesn't! Partly because they were "characters"—most of them—larger than life. It could be embarrassing sometimes, intimidating as well as rewarding. But it was never, never boring.

In those far-off days—seems a golden age now—relations were Very Important People whether you liked them or not. There was a saying current at the time, though only used by people like my old man and Uncle Ern—God gave us our relations, thank God we can *choose* our friends!

Whether you liked it or not Family was Family. And they'd call on you, without any warning, if they needed a sympathetic ear or an exchange of gossip. Of course there wasn't TV or radio in those days and in place of *The Archers* or *Coronation Street* you had the Family; a source of unlimited irritation, admiration, consternation and curiosity.

Uncle Tom was always held up to us as a man to admire. He had a regular income, a nice home, more principles than I can enumerate in a short story, and was next-door to being a minister.

When I say next-door, I mean he was a pillar of the Primitive Methodist, secretary of the Men's Bible Class and high up in the Rechabites. And when he had his accident, at work, and retired early with Compen, everybody admired him for beating the System.

To look at he was a tallish, long-legged man with a white moustache, steel-rimmed spectacles and an unrivalled knowledge of the Old Testament.

I usually met him when he was out for one of his walks. He was a great walker, Uncle Tom—not like my old man and me, we were ramblers, always ready to stop and stare. Uncle Tom was a *real* walker. Stepped out purposefully, swinging his stick and humming a favourite hymn.

He told me he preferred walking on hilltops to walking in valleys. You'd see him, striding along the skyline and praising the Lord, like some minor prophet. There was only one thing that militated against this idea of a minor prophet and that was his pipe. A short-stemmed briar which he would take out of his mouth to beat time with as he hummed or sang.

"Ah... Lewis, my boy!" he'd exclaim, like one minor prophet hailing another after years of separation. "Just the chap I wanted to see. I've got a little problem for you. Now, tell me... in the first book of Samuel, when David and Jonathan were reunited, the Good Book says they kissed and wept, one with another, until David *exceeded*... And that's my problem, Lewis—Exceeded what?"

I had to admit I didn't have his knowledge of the first Samuel but I would reckon he must have become very upset, overdone it perhaps.

Uncle Tom would puff whilst he considered, and then thank me for my help.

"I see your point, of course. But it doesn't seem quite in character, if you know what I mean. Not what I'd come to expect of the man. However, we've got to remember he was only human." And then, coming back to the here-and-now, "Have you tasted the air up here today?"

I admitted I hadn't actually,

consciously *tasted* it. It was a bit fresh, rather blowy.

"That's why it's special," he said. "Full of oxygen. Like wine. Better than wine because it's pure and free."

He threw out his chest and breathed deeply before returning his pipe to his mouth for a quick puff-puff to keep it alight. "Makes you glad to be alive," he said enthusiastically. "Washes away the cobwebs from the soul. It's God's gift, you know."

I didn't contradict him, perhaps I half-believed it, but anyway, when Uncle Tom was in the mood for it, he would quote Scripture at you till the cows came home. You'd think, to hear him, he was on first-name terms with 'em—Ezekiel, Habakkuk, Malachi and the rest. And, until I got to know him better, I used to think that the brook Kedron was down past Warmley somewhere—he always spoke of it as part of the scenery.

But—and there wouldn't be any story without that *"but"*— familiar as he was with the Old Testament, Uncle Tom was a bit of a fool when it came to women. His first marriage was satisfactory but not ecstatic, if you know what I mean, because Aunt Fanny had a horror of being touched. You might think he'd have found that out before he married her but I suppose he was too busy quoting Judges or Numbers. Anyway she went and died, leaving him a widower and, in a community like ours, a very good prospect. Never in want of a thing. His washing was done for him by one and his cooking by another and a third cleaned his house. Widows.

That was fine, until it was announced he was getting married again when, suddenly, the services stopped and he— poor man—wondered why.

She was a widow, down chapel, very respectable, a good housewife, though Gran, who was his sister, told me privately she thought this time he might have bitten off more than he could chew.

"Mind, I'm not saying there's anything wrong with her, I don't know much about the woman, but our Tom's very innocent about some things."

When she conveyed her doubts to Granfer he said it was no concern of his. "A bin married before," Granfer said gruffly. "Ought to know his own mind with all that Bible-study."

Gran said, Yes, he did but poor Fanny had spoilt him, fussed over him like a mother hen. It was "Tom won't have that" and "Tom doesn't care for this" until he'd come to expect it. "I reckon that's why he's getting married to Miriam," Gran said, "she reminds him of Fan."

"I should'a thought he'd've wanted a change," Granfer said. "She wadn't no oil-painting and they never had no children."

"Ah, well, that would have taken her interest away from him," said Gran. "He'll be getting three daughters with this 'un, from her first marriage. So he got a family, ready-made, without any o' the bother."

Granfer was not all that interested. He grunted and went out to see to his pigs. They were more predictable than human beings... and more profitable.

Within a week or two Uncle Tom brought her round to our cottage and then called in a few days later to hear Gran's opinion; or rather to listen, whilst he sang his intended's praises, which he did at great length whilst Gran stitched away in silence at a dress she was making.

Miriam was a model housewife, always hard at it, cleaning, washing, cooking. And neat as a new pin. You could eat your dinner off the floor in her house.

"Cleanliness ain't everything," Gran remarked.

"Next to Godliness, Sarah. I feel in my bones that she was Appointed for me, that this was Intended."

"Well, if you feel that, Tom, there's no more to be said."

When he was gone, Gran said "Cleanliness ain't everything as he'll find out." She seemed to know something that Uncle

Tom didn't. I asked her why but she shut up, as women do sometimes when they're in a stubborn mood. The fact was Gran was a wonderful woman but she wasn't a very good housewife. Our cottage was full of muddles and she looked on washing as she looked on toothache—as something to be endured.

There was a great wedding down the Prim and everybody said Tom was a lucky man—at any rate, the men did. It was noticeable that the older women kept quiet. As though they knew something. I was curious what it could be. And in the course of time I found out.

It must have been about six months later that Uncle Tom dropped in to see us.

"Miriam not with you?" Gran asked.

He took his pipe out of his mouth and looked at it as if it were a stranger. "I haven't been too well," he said. He looked as though he had been at death's door. A changed man. His glasses didn't sparkle with foresight, as they used to do. His walking-stick drooped. His voice was that of an ordinary man.

"Oh dear, I didn't know you'd bin bad," Gran said. "Still, I expect you bin well looked after."

"Oh, I haven't been bad in bed," he explained. "I've managed to get down to the allotment. Just as well since she won't have me in the house."

"Whyever not?" Gran put down her sewing and stared at him.

"Well I told you she likes to keep the house spotless. It's a mania with her—scrubbing and cleaning, from morn to night. If I come into the house she makes me take my boots off so as not to bring in dirt. I don't dare light my pipe because it spreads ash everywhere. A dirty habit, she calls it. I just happened to forget myself and tap out my pipe in her aspidistra and you'd have thought 'twas the end of the world. Said smoking was a heathen practice, not mentioned in the

Scripture—I tell you, Sarah, that cut me to the quick—having Scripture brought into it. Me, secretary of the Men's Bible Class!"

"Humiliating!" Gran murmured.

"So now I've got to turn out in every sort of weather to go for a smoke, in the hut down on my allotment, if the weather's inclement."

"But apart from that," she said, "everything's all right, isn't it?"

He looked round the room, saw I was deep in the *Wizard* or *Skipper* and looked at her meaningly. "No," he said. "I fear I've made a Terrible Mistake."

"Oh dear."

He took off his glasses and polished them on his sleeve.

"As you know, Sarah, being my sister, I've always been very fastidious about some things."

Gran nodded. "Yes you were always fussy as a boy—couldn't bear to get your hands dirty."

"That was one of the reasons I married her. She was so clean, so hard-working, so… serious."

"Well, what's the matter then?"

He leaned toward her, conspiratorially.

"She's got this… Occupation. Of course, I knew she was in great demand when I married her but I thought… when people came knocking for her, in the middle of the night and she got up and dressed and went off with 'em carrying a black bag… I thought… well, I thought they needed her for a laying-in… I thought she was helping bring young life into the world. Being such a dab-hand at cleaning and scrubbing she'd be just the woman for that sort of thing… that's what I thought until last Thursday."

Gran made encouraging noises.

"I came back from my allotment and took my boots off and they didn't hear me, in my stockinged feet. Miriam was saying to this woman, 'It was quite a surprise. He came up lovely with a good scrub, his hair cut and his beard trimmed. Under all that grime he wasn't a bad-looking man at all.' I knew at once who they were talking about. Old Joseph Jenkins. He'd passed on the week before. Sarah, I've married a laying-out woman."

"Oh dear," Gran said, "I wondered if you knew."

"Of *course* I didn't know. D'you think I could have married her, knowing that?"

"Somebody's got to do it."

"Yes, *somebody*. Not my wife. I taxed her with it and she gloried in it. Said she *enjoyed* her work. That finished me. I know somebody's got to do it but to enjoy it, that's not natural."

"They say she's very good at it," Gran said, "and I'm told laying them out pays better than helping at the laying-in."

He groaned.

"I shall never be able to touch her," he said with dignity. "I shall never let her touch me without thinking of where her hand's been and what it's been doing."

After he'd gone, Gran murmured to herself. "How are the mighty fallen!"

Women can be very cruel.

Uncle Jack

H E WAS MY GRAN WILSHIRE'S BROTHER, her younger brother—about fifty when I first knew him—a bachelor who lived by himself, in one room, in Staple Hill.

Some said Jack was shiftless because he never went to chapel, enjoyed a drink at the Red Lion and smoked when he should be keeping a wife and family, but I liked Uncle Jack.

He never said much, true and he couldn't read or write; but he was a kind and patient man. Usually out of work, just doing a bit for the Council, cleaning out Siston Brook or clearing away old mine tumps. Odd jobs.

When he was on the dole he'd pick blackberries and mushrooms in season to earn a few bob. And every Sunday, rain or shine, he'd come up to Gran's for a Sunday dinner. As his sister she felt responsible for him and she used to say "Well, at any rate I know he's had *one* good meal this week."

He'd bring her a bunch of cowslips or primroses because he knew she loved wild flowers and he hadn't anything else to give.

A bunch of primroses looked strange in his big gnarled hands. Out of place, if you know what I mean, as if they were growing in the roots of a tree.

"Brought 'ee a few flowers," he would mutter and Gran would take them, delicately, and blow her nose.

"Very thoughtful, Jack. Thanks!"

From a capacious pocket he'd take out something for me. A wooden soldier or some monkey nuts. It wasn't anything much, he just liked to bring something, no matter how trivial, to show willing, as they say.

Now I come to think of it, he was a tall man, long-legged but rather stooped with a blue scrage mark (half a bruise and half a scratch) on his forehead that showed he'd once been a miner. He head a grey, drooping moustache and always wore a cap. Except at meals, of course. As I said, he didn't talk much. At Sunday dinner Granfer did all the talking. Uncle Jack listened and nodded, very conscious of the fact that he was in another man's house, on sufferance, because my gran happened to be his only sister.

I've never known anybody with so much patience as Uncle Jack. You could see it, in his eyes. Deep down.

He'd spend hours mending one of my toys, unravelling a tangle of wool, making a kite or repairing a puncture.

And then the war came, the Second World War, and, for the first time in years, he had a regular job. In a factory, making castings. Until he returned, proper, and reverted to rambling the fields and lanes. Not so far, these latter years, however, because the work at the factory seemed to have sapped his spirit. He still came up to Gran's for his Sunday dinner but he said less than ever. I gathered that he still enjoyed his pipe and his pint. He was one of the last men I remember to smoke a clay pipe which was always short in the stem and in imminent danger of singeing his moustache.

Apart from his drinking and smoking Uncle Jack had only one interest and that was watching the cricket at Downend. He was there every Saturday, sat on one of the wooden seats against the wall of the churchyard...

He was there when he had his stroke and nobody noticed. Just went on sitting, propped against the wall—after the cricket had ended and everybody else had gone home. I don't know why Harry Nicholls didn't notice when he did his rounds. But he didn't. And Uncle Jack was still there next morning lying on the ground with the dew on him.

He was still alive so they took him to hospital. But he never spoke or recognised anybody and Gran said wherever he was, it wasn't there, in hospital…

Maybe it was Risca or Abertillery, one of the South Wales mining towns where he'd lived and worked as a young man. He had left our area because the pits were in a bad way and the wages were better in South Wales. The few times he waxed lyrical were when he spoke of Blaina and Risca and Abercarn. Then his voice would soften with emotion and they seemed to me to be wonderful, far-off, foreign places. Of course, when he'd been a young man there, before the First World War, the valleys had been full of life. Gran told me he had lived in lodgings at Risca when she'd sent word to him that their mother—a widow—was ill and had lost the use of her legs.

Straight away Jack left his work and his lodgings, all the life of the valleys, to come back home and look after his mother.

"He was a good son, our Jack," Gran would say. "Thought the world of his mother. Of course, when he came, he thought it wouldn't be for long, we all did. He wasn't to know she'd be like it for good.

"Done everything for her, mind. Wash and dress her, take her out in her wheelchair. Miles and miles. She'd never have lasted as long as she did but for he. I did what I could but there, I had a young family to look after and you know your granfer. He never liked me to be away from the house."

"Didn't he go back to Wales?" I asked her.

"Who, Jack? No; he never went back. A few letters came for'n. But he never had the heart to open 'em. Wouldn't let me read 'em for him, either. Didn't like the thought of admitting he couldn't read, see."

It wasn't until after he died of his stroke that she knew what was in them. They were love letters. From somebody called Annie. Well, not exactly love letters either. They reproached him for not writing to her, said she was anxious, asked him to let her know what was happening.

I didn't give it a thought until one day, about five or six years ago, I happened to be in Risca on business. Actually I'd come to know all the places Uncle Jack had talked about— Abertillery, Blaina, Abercarn. Bit of a disappointment after the glowing picture Uncle Jack had painted. Perhaps I'd come too late to see them when they were boom towns...

At Risca I spoke to an elderly lady behind the bar of a pub. Asked her if she'd lived there long. "All me life," she said. So then I asked her if she'd ever come across a Jack Lukins. A miner, from Bristol.

She went all red in the face.

"Yes, I did," she said. "I remember Jack Lukins all right. He served my sister Annie a real dirty trick. Left her and went back to Bristol. Going out together they were. Thinking of getting married. He told her some story about his mother being ill but whoever heard of a grown man like that going home to look after his mother? Wrote to him, too, but never had a reply. Broken-hearted, she was. Broken-hearted."

"What became of her?" I asked.

"What became of her, now? She married a local chap. Well, it wasn't any good waiting for Jack Lukins, was it? But she wasn't ever happy with him. Proper gone on Jack Lukins, she was. Why, d'you know him then?"

"He was my great-uncle. He's dead."

Well, she said, fancy that, wasn't it

a small world. I told her that his mother really *had* been ill, that it wasn't his fault.

"Well, but she wrote to him, he never replied."

"He couldn't read or write," I said.

She gasped. "You mean he was *illiterate?*" she said incredulously. "I should never have thought it. Illiterate. Well now, when you come to think of it, our Annie had a lucky escape."

My father's sister, Aunt Laura, whom Gran used to call "The Little Princess". She emigrated to Australia, but later in life yearned for nothing more than to return to where she was born.

The Incredible Story of Uncle Joe's Teeth

M Y UNCLE JOE WAS A SMALL MAN with a white moustache, no teeth, a trilby hat too large for him and a voice like a creaking gate. His voice used to fascinate me when I was a child. It seemed to originate in his nose then get lost somewhere, so that when it came out, eventually, it was almost ventriloquial. He was a great one for storytelling and his stories were as odd as his voice...

When I knew him he shared a cottage in our village with a legless lady, Miss Pitt, who was herself a remarkable character, so full of life and vitality that one forgot to feel sorry for her. She had been born without legs and contrived to do without them. Uncle Joe lived downstairs, she lived upstairs and they shared the kitchen. Sometimes he would push her out for a walk in her wheelchair but not often; she usually preferred to propel herself.

Naturally I was fascinated by the lady with no legs. How did she dress, I asked Uncle Joe, and do her cooking? How did she get downstairs?

"Oh, My Lar!" Uncle Joe creaked. "She daps around 'ere like a hindy-rubber ball. See 'er come down they stairs, my lad, and you've seen it all... Bumpety-bump, Bumpety-bump— you'd think she was gwayn to fall every secont. But do she? No fear. She swings herself down on her hans. Ay and out there in the kitchen, why, she's better than any of us. Does her washing, my boy, and up in her chair. One thing she *can't* do and that's peg the clothes out. That where Joe comes in. But apart from that ...well, there now, I be telling a lie. She do always welcome a start in her chariot. 'Come on, Joe,' she shouts, 'give us a start!' Not too vi-lent, o' course, but a gentle shove to get her started, up to shop or down to chapel or wherever she's off to."

I was never very sure how she earned her living but, looking back, I think she must have owned the house and let the downstairs rooms to my uncle. He had had more jobs than any other man I knew but they never seemed to last very long. After a month or two he would retire with a bad leg or a sprained arm, blood-poisoning or hernia. He was not a strong man and seemed prone to accidents. I remember being puzzled how he managed to get dermatitis in a corset factory and ulcers when manufacturing lavatory cleaner. But he was always willing to try something new.

His entire working life seemed to have been spent in a vain pursuit of employment stamps. You had to have a minimum number on the card before you could collect unemployment pay.

"If I could just get dree more," he croaked, "I should be a happy man."

Unfortunately three stamps represented three weeks' work and, by that time, Uncle Joe had run out of employments.

"Been droo the lot!" he exclaimed. "Bin everything but a doctor, a minister or a clerk." He was not too well fitted for clerical work since he was unable to read or write. It seemed to me that, if there was any justice, they would have let Uncle Joe earn his living telling stories but, alas, I was the only person who seemed to appreciate them, so this talent was unprofitable to him.

I remember one of his stories, typical of many, about his friend Albert. They had been friends since childhood but Albert was very ill and not expected to live. When Uncle Joe went to visit, Albert's family were sitting gloomily in the best parlour. They were dressed in their best clothes.

"Is 'er dead, then?" Joe wheezed.

"Not yet. But he can't last long. He's gone light in the head."

"I'll just go and see'n then. Pay me last respecs."

"Yes you better do that," said Albert's wife, "whilst there's still time."

Albert lay motionless, with his eyes open. He looked very pale. Joe sat down gingerly beside the bed and spoke to him.

"Alb," he said, "Alb, be you there?"

"Yes, Joe," came back a whisper. "Bist thee dead, too?"

"No, not yet," said Joe. "Nor bist thee. Neither of us, in fact. We'm still in the land of the living, Alb."

There was a wondering silence as Albert digested this fact.

"If I bain't dead," came the voice, "why's everything changed? I been thinking I must be dead and gone to heaven."

Uncle Joe whinnied. "They said you was light-headed."

"Well, what do 'em expect? Everything's gone different, Joe."

"Well, 'tis a bit different since last time I was here," admitted Joe, gazing around him. "Your missus has got new furniture and a carpet and new curtains."

"Is that what 'tis?" marvelled Albert. "I knew 'twas all different."

His eyes opened wide and he slowly sat up in bed. "But she can't have," he said. "Joe, we'm too poor. We can't afford furniture."

Uncle Joe cackled like a couple of witches in a haunted house.

"Hey, I'll bet she got the furniture on the strength of thy life insurance," he said.

Slowly a flush spread over Albert's pallor.

"Joe," he said, "I bet thee bist right. She was always a dapster for the penny-a-week boys. Joe, my son, I'll come back and haunt her."

I waited but Uncle Joe was busy filling his pipe. "Did he?" I asked impatiently. "Did he come back?"

"No need to. He hadn't gone nowhere. He were up and about in a week, arter that."

"What about the new furniture?"

"Hee, hee! Had to go back, my son, every stick of it."

"I'll bet his wife didn't like that."

"Not she. Blamed me for it. Said I should have let'n die in peace, let'n think he'd gone before. 'Tis the nearest he'll ever get to heaven, she said. I been forbade the house ever since," he added gloomily.

"Poor old chap," commented my grandmother. "You never was a great favourite of the ladies, Joe."

Joe agreed.

"I just bain't a ladies' man, missis," he said.

There he was wrong. Within six months, Miss Pitt had taken over Albert's place as his Sunday companion, only it wasn't to the Black Horse that *they* went, but the Zion Methodist Church... And they came away from it before long as man and wife. They were both in their fifties, so it wasn't exactly passion which prompted their joining hands in wedlock. Somehow Joe became less of a character after that.

Did I mention that she was energetic? Well, Uncle Joe soon discovered some disadvantages to that. He was fitted for false teeth, and had to attend Chapel regularly. His stories lost their relish as he was made respectable, and from being a character you might have mistaken him for anybody. It's a terrible thing, normality, but Uncle Joe came quite near to it. Only when Miss Pitt—and we still call her that, Mrs Lukins didn't seem right—only when she was out of the way did Uncle Joe take out his teeth and become human!

"Don't let 'er bury me with 'em," he'd whisper. "I shan't be comfortable in me coffin if they'm there."

Somehow these false teeth weren't him.

Ah well, all flesh is grass, and Uncle Joe joined the immortals long ago.

I can't reveal the secret between the undertaker and me. Anyway it's a gruesome subject, but I'm happy to say that his false teeth didn't accompany him into the hereafter. I disposed of them in Aunt Lil's fish-tank, and she, poor soul, being very short-sighted, thought they were pebbles. The goldfish didn't seem to mind either. They swam in and out of Uncle Joe's molars with out any fear at all!

Granfer in the orchard with Lizzie and Gran.
Lizzie lived in the village and ran errands for
Gran. Her mental development had been arrested
at the age of four when she discovered her
mother's crumpled body, dead at the bottom of
the well.

Scrumping

"**S**TOLEN FRUITS TASTE SWEET" was a saying with my gran. Not that she condoned theft. It was just a fact of life, so far as she was concerned. It was certainly true of scrumping....

Put crudely "scrumping" is pinching apples.

But, of course, there's more to it than that. They must be taken from an orchard which its owner thinks is impregnable, they mustn't be "fallers" and only apples that are ripe and picked on the bough will do. Oh, yes, and you have to climb the trees to pick 'em.

Now you may think that, because my granfer had an orchard that was a prime target. I would be on the side of the owner but then you didn't know my granfer. If I asked for an apple he'd give me some maggoty "faller". The best fruit was kept for the paying customers. If I wanted the best I had to join the scrumpers.

That's how I found myself in company with Shirty and Cliff, planning a raid on Granfer's orchard. I knew it was a sort of treachery but that only made it more exciting. If we were caught the other two might be walloped but it would be worse for me; Granfer would keep on about it. Never let me forget it.

There was a very thick hawthorn hedge round our orchard. But I knew a way in and I knew the time we could do it. If we cut across Haycock's garden we could climb the old stone wall, swing across on the low boughs of the old ash tree—and there was treasure for the taking. Pippins and Underleaves, Tom Putts and Roseberries. Thousands of 'em, waiting to be picked.

"I'll go first," Cliff said: "spy out the ground."

He nipped across Haycock's garden, taking care to avoid treading on a broccoli, knowing it was safe because it was

Saturday and the Haycocks always went to the Regal on Saturdays, climbed the wall and spied out the land. It must have been all right because he beckoned us on. We swung down on the lower branches of the warty old ash tree, into the cool deep greens of the orchard grass.

There were apples everywhere. "Fallers" scrunched under your feet when you walked and Shirty was all for stuffing our pockets and making a quick getaway. But Cliff said No, that wasn't right—we must climb the trees and pick 'em proper. He chose the Tom Putt tree for himself, I chose the broad old Underleaf with its boughs that swept the ground. Shirty said he was scared of heights so he stayed on the ground to keep "cavey".

We were all busy scrumping when suddenly a giant roar broke the silence.

"*Hi! What be up to?*"

It was Granfer and he carried a stick.

I don't know if I've ever explained about Granfer. He was a big man. Near on twenty stone. Tall and broad, truculent, with a voice like thunder. The other kids called him Chooky because he kept pigs and called "Chooky, chooky, chooky" when it was feeding time. But they never called him that to his face. Nobody ever did.

Naturally we didn't tell him what we were up to. Shirty fled. Up in the Tom Putt tree Cliff couldn't move. He froze. Tried to look like part of the trunk. As for me, I was concealed by leaves, but I could hear him puffing and blowing down below.

"Lar-blass me soul, thee cassn't leave it ten minutes but they'm up to their tricks. 'Tis the kids from the New Buildings. Can't leave people's property alone. If I do ketch 'em, if I do ketch 'em… I'll have the hide off 'em!"

Cliff must have moved slightly in his precarious perch up the Tom Putt because an enormous great apple came down with a thud at Granfer's feet.

The old man looked suspiciously up into the tree. Fortunately his sight wasn't too good.

"If thass somebody up there," he shouted, "thee's better

Granfer's orchard

come down whilst thee's got the chance." Cliff didn't move. "Whoever you be, I'll give thee summat to remember," Granfer repeated.

This didn't encourage Cliff to give himself up. If anything, it made him more determined than ever to stay where he was.

"Well, if thee 'ont come down, I'll come up there and fetch thee."

Granfer went to fetch a ladder and that was our chance. As soon as he went off in the direction of the pigsties Cliff shouted "Come on then—run for it!" He dropped out of his tree and I from mine and we raced for the wall.

Granfer turned and waved his stick. *"Stop! Come back 'ere! I knows who you be, I'll tell your father. Stop!"*

But of course, we didn't stop. Stopping was the last thing in our heads. We ran for our lives, helter-skelter for the wall, across Haycock's garden—and we didn't feel safe until we were in the sanctuary of our Secret Hideout in the elderberry bush down Tenacres.

Shirty was waiting for us, in the green gloom.

"He never caught you, then ?"

"No, we waited till his back was turned," Cliff said. "He said he knew who we were. D'you reckon he did?"

"He's pretty short-sighted," I said. "P'raps he only said that. I shall know when I goes in for tea."

At tea-time Granfer was in a mood. His eyebrows were down and his chest was bad. He clumped about, making unnecessary noise,

"What's 'a matter, Fred?" Gran asked.

"'Tis they boys," he grumbled. "After me apples. Out in the archut clambering about in the trees, bold as brass."

"Didn' you ketch 'em?"

"No, I didn't. They'm as quick as ferrets. But let 'em wait. I knows who they be."

"Come on, Lewis, you haven't *touched* your bread and

butter!" Gran said. "Eat up or you'll never be a big boy."

I wasn't all that interested in food, just then. Wouldn't be until I knew whether Granfer had seen me. By the end of tea-time I knew he hadn't. And I was just congratulating myself on a lucky escape when Gran noticed a tear in my shirt. I could feel her eyes on it and at any moment expected her to say "How d'ee come to tear the shirt then?"

If she did, Granfer would know for certain because he found a bit of material caught up in the bark of the Underleaf tree.

Gran knew, but she didn't say anything. She just winked.

"Who d'ee reckon they were?" she asked innocently.

Granfer was quite confident.

"I could tell by the shape on 'em. 'Twas they Hawkins boys, proper hardened they kids be. I shall tell their mother. Mrs Hawkins 'll hear about this."

Gran looked doubtful.

"Shouldn't be in too much of a hurry to do that," she said. "She's a funny-tempered woman, that Mrs Hawkins. Might take umbrage. And—let's see now—she's a good customer o' yours, ain't she?"

Granfer snorted with vexation. He knew she was right and, as usual, resented it.

"You've burnt this cake!" he said. "Currrants is like bits o' grit. They'd break my teeth if I had any."

When we were alone together, Gran said "Stolen fruits taste sweet, eh?"

"We never got none, except Shirty, and he wouldn' share."

"You chose the wrong time," Gran said. "You ought to know better. Best time's after dinner when he's having his nap."

The Secret of the Red Hand

AROUND GRAN'S COTTAGE there was a maze of little wandering lanes with a sprinkling of cottages, beyond the reach of city suburbs. Gran and Granfer and their friends referred scathingly to these red brick suburbs as the New Buildings. They remembered the fields they were built on—Tenacres and Gapper's and the Cherry Orchard.

Actually, I belonged to both worlds, that of the cottages, lanes and long gardens and that of the New Buildings. I knew the children of the village and the kids on the new estate. But, to tell you the truth, I never really decided which world I really belonged to.

They were very different: the village boys were quieter, more secretive, wandered east in search of the country: but the kids of the New Buildings had an intense and lively life in their own bit of street—there was warfare between one street and another round the corner, with a street lamp as a sort of totem pole because that was the centre of social life.

In those days you had to belong to a Gang. I belonged to a very inoffensive collection of five boys who lived in our lanes and, because we were seldom raided or invaded by gangs from the New Buildings, we became complacent.

That's why we were shocked to discover the Note, one day, in our hidey-hole, our special place, at the back of Englands' cottage. A nice convenient little place it was; a gap in the stones about three inches across, six inches long and four inches deep. The footpath to tripe-alley went along the back of Englands' so you weren't trespassing or anything. It was their chimney—you knew that because if you laid your hand on the stones in cold weather, you could feel the warmth. Just to think that the other side of that wall old Mr and Mrs England would be sitting, either side of the fire, he smoking, she knitting! We sometimes put our ears to the crack but either they never spoke to each other or there was a lot more stones in the way—you couldn't hear a word!

Still, as I say, there it was—a hole in the wall. And we'd always regarded it as our secret hiding place, known to nobody but us five. Until we found the Note... It was Shirty who found it. He would. He was always looking for small treasures: that was why he had that sort of hang-dog look. He walked along with his eyes on the ground, not because he was ashamed of his school report or his dropped catches, but because he'd once found a sixpence in the mud and several buttons which he kept in a tin. After all, he said, you never knew! Shirty lived in hopes of a great find—a jewel-thief might have been on the run, closely pursued by the police, with his back to the wall. He demonstrated, "What'd he do with the stolen diamond? Why, shove it in this hole."

As he spoke, his eyes grew round with wonder. His fingers explored the hole in the wall.

"Whassermatter?" we asked. "Hurt your finger, have 'ee? Get it caught?"

We watched as he withdrew his hand from the hole in the wall, holding a crumpled note.

"Blimey, iss only a bit o' paper," he said disgustedly. "I thought it might's bin a poun' note."

"Wait a minute," said Den, our leader. "There's some words writ on it."

We craned over his shoulder to read the wording scrawled in capitals—WARNING. DO NOT TOUCH. I AM WATCHING YOU. THIS IS MY PLACE. SINED—THE RED HAND."

"It says he's watching us," Clarence said.

We looked at the blackberry bushes, the elder tree and Englands' old shed suspiciously.

"We better git off quick," said Dennis who didn't like the sound of the Red Hand. "I bet it's one of they gangs up in the New Buildings. I've heard about 'em. They'm rough."

"A boy at school said they holds people hostage, for blackmail," said Don. It sounded very plausible and alarming and I didn't contradict. Because my mum and dad lived in the New Buildings I knew some of the boys and girls who lived there and they never mentioned gangs taking hostages. All I said was "I dunno. They say there's a gang up in Holly Grove but they don't usually come down this far. They just fights the boys in Ashgrove and plays football down the Rec."

"It wouldn't be them," Don said. "The Red Hand sounds more like criminals. Don't look like kids' writing."

"Less put'n back in the wall and run for it," Shirty said. He was not a hare, more of a survivor.

"No," Don said, "it's our hidey-hole and we got to show whoever 'tis that we ain't afraid."

"How?" we asked.

"By writing our own message on the back. Who's got a pencil?"

Clarence found a stump of indelible pencil in among the marbles and five stones and bits of string in his pocket, and Don licked it and wrote:

THIS IS OUR PLACE. WE ARE WAITING FOR YOU. WATCH OUT. THE GANG OF TEN.

"That'll put the wind up 'em," Dennis said.

"But there's only five of us," Clarence pointed out.

"Well, they're not to know that, are they?"

"I reckon we ought to put down that we're grown-ups and that if we ketches 'em we'll torture 'em," Dennis said.

"No, they'd know we was kids if we said we was grown-ups," Don said scornfully.

He put the note back in the hole and we looked at each other and then at the undergrowth. Then, horrified at our own foolhardiness, we fled. As we ran, Dennis puffed "W... What we runnin' for?"

Don stopped running and we all stopped. By Buller Howe's cow-shed.

"One o' us'll have to keep watch," he said.

There was no great eagerness to be the watcher. Some talk of drawing lots and then we decided to take it in turns, hiding in the old loft over Englands' hen house. Well, of course, we couldn't be there when we were at school or running errands, but we devised a rota, according to which two of us shared a watch. It was when I was sharing a watch with Dennis, two or three days later, that they came to collect...

We were lying there, in the dust and cobwebs, with bits of hay and straw on our school jerseys, when there was a movement in the blackberry bushes.

"It's them!" said Dennis.

"Ssh! They might hear us."

We held our breath, prepared to retreat out at the back through Englands' fowl run when a small, red-haired, freckle-faced little girl crept out of the bushes, tip-toed to the wall and took out the note.

"Issa girl!" Dennis said, disgustedly.

"She might be a decoy," I said hopefully. "The real gang might've sent her. Let's watch what she does."

She read the back of the note. We heard her gasp. Then she ran off down the path, past Dyer's.

"Come on then," shouted Dennis, suddenly brave. "Let's follow."

Leaving cover, we followed her at a safe distance until she disappeared into a big old elderberry in the lane down past Smithy's.

"We'll surround her," Dennis said. So we approached the bush from both sides, pushed aside the leaves and there she was, sitting on a branch, a few feet from the ground, thinking herself safe.

"We got you captured," I said.

Dennis said, "You'd better tell us where your gang are. If you don't, we shall... we shall... clip you one."

The little girl was not at all scared.

"Not afraid o' you," she said. "Two kids. Where's the others? It says ten."

"Back in our den," said Dennis, "waiting for us to take you back. We got ropes and that, back there."

"You can't scare me," she said. "I only got to whistle and the Red Hand'll come and rescue me."

"Go on, there ain't any Red Hand," I said.

She put two fingers in her mouth, like an expert, and whistled. It was a piercing whistle, too, astonishing in such a small girl.

Dennis and I seized her, holding her arms and dodging the kicks she aimed at us.

"Help!" she shouted.

There was the sound of running feet. We let go for a minute and she pushed us aside and ran. When we looked out, there were three of them, all girls, the other two smaller than our captive. A wild chase followed, they all went different ways and I found myself on my own pursuing the freckle-faced girl. Out into the New Buildings. Up and down roads. She could run, that girl! Several times I nearly got her but she was like an eel and eventually went to earth in number 55 Maypole Drive, a red brick semi-detached. I waited outside trying to look sinister—not so easy for a boy of ten with short trousers, a rumpled jersey and a tendency to blush.

Somehow I knew she'd come out again. And she did. With her big brother—red-haired and truculent.

"Thass him!" she said, pointing at me. "Chased me with a gun, he did! There's nine more of 'em..."

"Hullo, Bert," I said.

"Hullo," he said. "Whassamatter then? She bin teasing you?"

We went to the same school, played for the same football team.

"She said she had a gang," I explained. "The Red Hand. Are you the Red Hand?"

"No I'm not," Bert said.

"There was a note, writ in blood," I said.

"That wasn't blood," Bert scoffed. "That was her. She pinched our dad's red ink and he bin blaming me for it. You wait," he told her, "when I tell'n who pinched it he'll dock your pocket money."

Avoiding his grasp, she fled inside the house and, ten seconds later, her face appeared at a bedroom window. Snub nose and freckled face flushed with anger, she stuck her tongue out at us.

"Boys!" she shouted. "You're all the same—rotten!"

I went back to tell the others that I'd solved the mystery of the Red Hand—only it came out a bit different in the telling—Bert became a great hulking brute of a bloke who came at me with a pickaxe. I said I noticed, as I dodged the blow, that one of his hands was red.

This went down well with the other four. They guessed it was made up but they liked a good story as much as I did and it confirmed what they had always thought: that the people who lived in the New Buildings were a strange lot. You were only safe, the gang decided, if you kept to the lanes.

We Have Been Here Before

HAVE YOU EVER MET SOMEBODY, or been in a situation, when you've said to yourself: "This has happened before" or "We've met before somewhere"? Only it turns out that it hasn't and you didn't? All very strange.

Some say it is a thing called precognition, the result of unconscious clairvoyance, some say it's because you've dreamed it beforehand. There was one chap (I've forgotten his name) who said it was due to parallel time scales and there are those who think it *has* all happened before—in a previous existence.

Whatever the explanation, it does happen. It happened to me first when I was six. I'd started infants' school, and in the playground I met John. John Ayres. We looked at each other and I knew we'd met before. He knew as well. Right from that first glance we were friends.

I'd never had a proper friend before, only playmates, so John was special. We didn't have to talk, that was the wonder of it: there was a sort of telepathy between us. We always knew what the other was thinking without needing to put it into words. We sat at the same desk, of course, and I used to call for him on my way to school.

He lived quite close to the school. I was some distance away so, every morning, regular, I would

When I was a boy...

call for him and every day, after school, walk home with him. He would vanish into their house with a wave of the hand which was also, I felt, somehow a gesture of dismissal. That, and the fact that he never, *ever*, smiled, used to puzzle me.

We never met outside school and that should have puzzled me, too; but it didn't. Evenings and weekends I was a normal active boy. At school I forgot my playmates because there was John. I'm pretty sure he hadn't any playmates at all. He was a solitary boy, pale-faced, delicate features, high wide forehead and frank brown eyes. They were soft and yet deep, those eyes, and you got the impression that he was terribly vulnerable. Somehow you felt afraid for him—at least I did.

Myself, I wasn't like him at all. I was freckled and watchful; sullen, Miss Cliff called me, but she never saw me when I was merry. Nor did John come to that—he was a very serious little boy. Even at that age I was inclined to be a bit vague at times, absent-minded...

I remember they were building a craft room or something in the playground and we were warned of the consequences if we went anywhere near the workings, particularly the piles of bricks.

Of course we hadn't any intention of going near the piles of bricks. John and I weren't hardened like some of the kids but, as I say, I was awfully absent-minded. Wandering along, deep in thought, I heard the sound of running feet and John pulling my sleeve.

"What is it?" I asked.

Before he had time to tell me the whistle blew and Miss Cliff descended on us like an avenging angel.

"Naughty boys!" she shrieked. "How *dare* you! After you've been warned!"

We were dragged into school, made to stand in separate corners and "kept in".

I tried to tell Miss Cliff that it wasn't John's fault, he'd only tried to rescue me. And he tried, very timidly, to tell her that I hadn't meant to, only forgot. She told us to hold our tongues. "Naughty, wicked boys," she told the class. "All of you heard my warning, didn't you?"

"Yes, Miss Cliff," they chanted.

"And you saw these two boys go right up to a pile of bricks?"

"Yes, Miss Cliff!"

"I intend to punish them. Severely. I don't want *any* of you— ANY of you," she repeated, "to speak to them for a whole week."

"No, Miss Cliff."

It wasn't really much of a punishment. We didn't want to talk to them anyway—we were different, John and I. Being sent to Coventry only brought us closer together.

When she saw that it was ineffective, Miss Cliff decided to punish us in a different way. She convinced herself that we had a bad effect on each other, so she split us up. John had to go and sit with Walt Foreman, the class bully, who pinched you when she wasn't looking, and I had to share a form with Lizzie Bateman who picked her nose.

The minute we were liberated from school, though, John and I met and walked home together. We didn't hold hands because that would have caused derision but we took comfort from each other, somehow, and although we never put it into words, we realised Miss Cliff was more than a mere teacher at school—she was the embodiment of some old evil, she was intolerance. We had known her before somewhere …somewhere else.

…And then, one morning, John wasn't waiting for me at his gate. I assumed he must have gone on because I was a bit late that morning on account of mother making me run an errand. I ran the rest of the way, hoping to catch up with him but I only just got there when the whistle blew and we had to form up and march inside.

When Miss Cliff called the Register, no-one answered for John Ayres. She looked over the top of her glasses. His seat was empty.

"Absent," she said, putting down an "A" instead of a tick, and went on with her roll-call. I wondered where he was but didn't like to call and ask.

He didn't come to school that day or the next or the rest of that week. I thought for certain he'd be back on Monday so I went early and waited outside his gate. He didn't come and when I knew it was getting on time I plucked up courage and knocked at the door. I had never been inside the house. His mother, when she came to the door, looked unhappy. Her eyes were red.

"Yes, what is it?" she asked.

"Is John coming to school?"

"No, he's not," she said banging the door in my face.

If I live to be a hundred—and I don't think that's very likely— I shall never get over the shock.

I wondered if I'd said or done anything wrong. Perhaps she'd heard that Miss Cliff thought we were bad for each other. Maybe she thought I was rough...

For the next few days I lived in a dream. John didn't return to school and I didn't dare call for him. And then when we were having dinner one day, mum said "There's a lot of that scarlet fever about. Somebody in the butcher's told me a little boy went down with it. Goes to your school. Name of Ayres."

My heart thumped in my chest.

"Where is he?" I asked.

"Oh, they took'n away. Down the isolation hospital. Why, do you know him?"

"Where's the isolation hospital?"

"Ham Green," she said. "Miles away. Two or three buses."

It sounded like the other side of the world and I was even more absent-minded than ever. Miss Cliff said I was hopeless and kept me in.

It may have been a few days later that she called out John Ayres, as usual, from the Register and then recollected something and struck out his name. I was horrified. She had put a line through my friend's name as though he had never been there.

"Lewis Wilshire," she repeated and then, looking over her glasses, "speak up, boy. Haven't lost your voice as well as your senses?"

The class tittered, dutifully. I was silent. I couldn't think, couldn't feel—suddenly I had to get away.

Before she could stop me I jumped up and ran out of the room, out of the school, down the road. I couldn't go home. They would ask me questions. So I went to my den, my secret place in the middle of an old elder bush. There I could weep in peace: for John because I knew, with a child's certainty, that he was dead; and for myself because I'd lost a friend.

Later in the day I went home.

"Wherever have you been?" mother asked. "I s'pose you had dinner with a friend?"

I nodded.

"You ought to have more thought," she said. "I was wondering all sorts of things, thinking you might have been knocked down or ill. You never know these days, from one hour to the next. They were saying down the greengrocer's about that little boy, the one who had scarlet fever..."

"How is 'er?" father asked.

"Poor soul!" mother said in her holy-holy voice. "He passed on."

At that moment father got a kipper bone stuck in his throat. A good job too, or they would have seen the tear in my eye.

"He must of went to your school," father said. "Did you know en?"

I said I did but not that he was my friend.

Already I'd learned the dangers of giving yourself away. They would have expected nerves and nightmares. There would have been soothing reassurances and the last thing I wanted was sympathy. I knew it would only be a question of time anyway. This kept on happening to John and me. It had happened before and it would happen again... sometime, somewhere.

Since then I've grown up, got married, brought up a family and had many friends. But I've never met another John and now I doubt if I shall, this time round.

Reflecting on life with the aid of a pipe in Vassalls Park

Ashen Faggots

HE WAS ABOUT FIFTY, AS I REMEMBER HIM. Worked for a brewery, in Bristol then. A keen gardener. Lived up the lane from Gran and Granfer. We called him Coz.

Funny thing, he didn't like trees. Some don't. People say the world's divided into tree-lovers and tree-haters. Unlike my granfer who loved trees, Coz hated them.

Mind, there were a lot of people who said Granfer went too far. Our place looked like a miniature forest. There were apple, pear and plum trees in the orchard, the bay tree by the front door, an old lilac that sprouted suckers until it was practically a forest in itself… And that was only the beginning!

Hawthorn hedges formed a barrier between us and the rest of the world, and growing out of the hedges were ash trees, pollarded, to provide Granfer with kidney bean sticks. One of these, with a huge mis-shapen head and a trunk that was gnarled and scarred, grew up alongside Coz's garden.

He hated that tree, did Coz. Said it shut all the light out of his front room, used up the goodness in the soil and made his rose bed wilt and—what was worse—gave Mrs Coz the collywobbles when she came down the garden path on moonlit nights.

It was the shape, I suppose. Like a huge, hairy gnome. A bit sinister, at night, with the moon behind it— almost human. She

said it reminded her of Old Nick though I don't see how she could know that, myself, without having seen the man.

"He do kip all the light out, Mr Wilshire," Coz explained. "I'd be most obliged to 'ee if you could see your way to cut 'n down."

"Nuthin' the matter with thik tree," Granfer said firmly. "He's on *my* land and there he'll stay. 'Tis a marker for me boundary."

"I'd put a post up in place of 'n," Coz hazarded. "He do give my missus the creeps."

"Hrmp!" Granfer snorted, dismissing Coz's wife without speaking a word.

"You know how women takes these things, Mr Wilshire. She do reckon that tree's—well, sort of—suggestive, if you know what I mean!"

"Silly woman!"

Granfer had no time to waste on women's fancies. He walked away.

"Why don't you want to cut down the old ash, Granfer?" I asked.

"That there tree," said Granfer decisively, "is more of a friend to I than Coz will ever be."

"How's that?"

He then drew breath through his nose ferociously as though he were going to breathe fire. Stopping, he put his hand on my shoulder and proceeded to explain his philosophy of trees.

"People don't realise about trees, my son. They'm longer-lived than we. That tree, now, was planted by my granfer. I know he's old and he's a queer shape but I've had hundreds and thousands of bean poles off that tree and I bain't goin' to cut 'n down just to please Coz and Lillie."

"Still, if it keeps out the light..."

"Ha, thass a load of codswallop! The truth is, Coz and she don't *like* trees. He's a gardener, as you do know, and keen gardeners don't like nuthin to grow that they can't cook in a pot and, as for she," he snorted, "she got it in for that tree because he reminds her of summat she don't want to know about. That's why they got no children," he said darkly, but added "however, you'm too young to know about such things."

Granfer didn't like Lillie because Lillie complained that his pigs created a smell. He could never understand the "niceness" of people: the kind who wrinkle up noses when they got a whiff of some good honest country smell... To Granfer the pigs were something to be proud of, the trees were extensions of himself. *His* property. Along with everything else on his land—the wild flowers and weeds, herbs and caterpillars, birds and hedgehogs! He had a fatherly feeling for them and when a blackbird or thrush built its nest in the green bay tree or the hawthorn hedge Granfer looked on it as his tenant. It became a duty to protect it from cats and small boys. Even the owl who always nested in the open roof over the outside water closet was part of his empire. When it hooted,

Coz's cottage with Granfer's beyond

of an evening, he puffed his pipe complacently. His owl was looking for mice over Albert Howe's orchard and doing its share to keep the population of rodents at bay.

Lillie hadn't any time for birds.

"Nasty dirty things, they be," she said, "dropping their muck on my clean washing and stealing my Coz's peas as soon as he puts 'em in."

Once, when she had complained to Granfer directly about the pigs, he had asked sternly if she ever ate bacon.

"Yes, yes," she fluttered, "but I don't see..."

"Thee can't get bacon without pigs!" Granfer told her. "The smell—and 'tis a good honest smell, to my mind—is the price you got to pay for having bacon."

If he hadn't stalked away she would have told him that she had to suffer the smell but still had to *buy* her bacon. And the smell wouldn't be quite so unbearable if he would re-site the muck heap nearer *our* cottage and further away from *hers*.

But she didn't get the chance to explain because Granfer had walked away. He had no patience with silly women.

In the course of time Granfer gave up keeping pigs, but he obdurately clung to the ash tee. Must have irritated Mr and Mrs Coz for upward of thirty year, and then the old man died. Gran was too kind to resist her neighbours' entreaties and the tree was cut down.

"Ah, you can see where you be now," said Coz, "without all that foliage. And my Lillie can go down our garden path at night without the fear of evil coming over her."

It was almost as if a dark force had been lifted from their lives. No strange shadows on the path now when the moon was full. And without the ash tree, birds lacked a perch from which they could spy out Coz's garden and his wife's washing.

And then he fell ill. They said it was a seizure. All the life seemed to go out of him. Coz retired from work and looked at his garden with lack-lustre eyes.

One day his wife asked me if I'd come in and see him write his will. He was feeble by that time and she whispered to me that he had a tendency to wander, pointing at her head to indicate where the wandering took place.

I tried to be cheerful, said the weather was good for the time of year, but he could only bemoan the neglect of his garden.

"Can't get down to it, see," he said, "since I bin took. They birds is playing havoc, no doubt, wiv nobody to scare 'em off." He sighed. "All I can do is sit in me chair and look out droo the window. Day in, day out. Sit and look at the same piece of sky."

"Still," I said, "at any rate you can see the sky now that the old ash tree's gone."

He shook his head.

"I use to be able to lie in bed and see the birds in among the leaves, courting and catching flies. The leaves did dance in the wind when 'twas blowing and, in the winter, I've seen the hoar frost turn thik branches to silver."

The Lemon Pippin tree whose bumper harvest one year caused yet more bad blood between Granfer and Coz.

"Rambling," Lillie murmured. "He always wanted 'n cut down."

"Now the ol' tree's gone," said Coz, "and 'tis my turn next. 'A life for a life' as my ol' father use to say."

Lillie escorted me to the door.

"You get it wrote out proper," she said, "and he can put his cross on the bottom. Never had the benefit of education, my Coz. You mustn't take no notice of his ramblings. He got that old tree on the brain since he bin took bad. They'da get some queer fancies when folks is like that—says he can see pictures in the fire when we burns the logs."

"Ah, they'll be from the old ash tree. How do they burn?" I asked, remembering that Gran had let Coz have the logs after they'd cut down the tree.

"Lovely," she said. "Throws out a wonderful lot o' heat. Flames do shoot out of 'em, all colours of the rainbow, in little jets and then you'da get one as do just smoke and smoke and won't blaze at all. My Coz, he do sit there and gaze at the fire and sometimes he'll start up and say 'Lillie, come and look at this! In the flames, 'Tis for all the world like old Mrs Thomas the postman's wife!' Or it might be his own father or mother! Wandering, that's what 'tis. His mind's wandering."

After we'd made out the will, Lillie said she hoped it would be long years before anyone need look at it. Coz asked weakly how many logs were left.

"Not many," she said. "Enough for three or four days."

"Three or four days," he meditated.

"After that we shall use the coal," she said brightly. "There's half a ton in the coalhouse—plenty for the winter and 'tis barely New Year."

"Three or four days," the old man muttered. "Only three or four days."

She shook her head as she opened the door for me.

"I shall be glad to see the last of that old tree," she said.

"He've brought us nothing but bad luck from first to last."

Coz went with the last of the logs, in three or four days, on old Christmas Eve. As he predicted, it was a life for a life.

Footnote

Ash trees were worshipped by prehistoric man. It was considered sacrilege to destroy them because each tree had its familiar spirit and they used to appease this spirit, annually, by burning ashen faggots.

An annual ceremony takes place on old Christmas Eve at a pub in Somerset, the King William IV, Curry Rivel. Having cut ashen faggots from a growing tree, local people bind them into bundles with hazel wands.

On January 5th they gather together, in the pub, and throw these bundles on to an open fire. As the bonds of willow burst they drink a toast to the ash tree then go out wassailing round the parish.

Lush and overgrown: the view from the back of Granfer's cottage

Taken Short

THE TROUBLE IS YOU AREN'T ALLOWED TO TELL STORIES— even true stories—about some things. So I warn you, here and now, if you're very prim and proper you'd better move on to the next story...

As I've said before, my old man was funny in some ways.

He didn't like heights. He didn't like animals. He loved hates. But what I haven't told you is that he had a weak bladder.

It irritated Mother. She said it was a millstone round our necks. I don't know about that—it was an embarrassment.

"Why can't you be like other people?" she'd say. "They don't spend half their lives looking for toilets."

"I can't help it, Alice," he'd groan. "P'raps I got a weakness there."

So whilst everybody else was paddling in the sea at Weston or fishing for tiddlers at Snuffy Jacks, we'd be looking for a toilet for Father.

"It's always the same with him," Mother would grumble. "D'you know, he even let me down at our wedding. Downend church, it was. And he'd no sooner got there than he was asking the vicar for the toilet."

"They never had one," Father mourned. "You'd think they'd have some consideration even in holy places."

"Certainly not," Mother snapped. "They expect people to have a sense of discretion. Your father's never had any dignity," she told us.

We didn't need to be told that. My sister and I had witnessed his sudden—not to say, frantic—departures from school prizegivings, harvest festivals and railway stations. There was that time he was left at Temple Meads when he was taken short on an excursion to Weston.

As Mother said, "Only your father could leave us in the lurch at a time like that. It's not as if there weren't toilets on the train."

"They was all full up," he said, "with people dodging the ticket collector."

We couldn't go for a walk in the country without Father demanding facilities. Up on top of the Mendips. Down at Shepardine. In Goblin Combe. It was father same old story... as soon as were far from what he called the "maddening" crowds... "where can I spend a penny?"

And it wasn't just the inconvenience of it. My old man was fastidious with it. He couldn't go behind a hedge or a tree like other people, it had to be a proper toilet. Apart from the impropriety there was the danger. Father had a thing about insects. Wasps and bees were dangerous and they might be lurking anywhere.

"You don't have to worry about being stung there," Mother would say. "It's your tongue you want to watch. They say a bee sting on your tongue can be fatal. You ought to keep your mouth shut."

But that was something Father couldn't do. He was never silent for long. Mother used to swear that the two minutes' silence on Armistice Day was the only time Father was awake and silent in the whole year.

When we went away on holiday, Father's first exploration was not to find the sea or the beaches. More important to him was where the toilets were. The scenery could be magnificent but if there were no toilets my old man was desolate. He could never understand why, when they gave information about so many things, the guides failed to mention where the Ladies and Gents were situated.

I humorously suggested writing a whole series—West Country Toilets, In Search of Convenience, A Guide to Historic WCs. One could even give them a star rating.

It was supposed to be a joke but Father didn't think it was

funny. He thought they would be useful.

One of the more difficult moments was back in the 1950s. At the Theatre Royal in King Street. Pantomime.

No sooner had the curtain gone up than Father was whispering "Alice—you didn' happen to notice where *they* was when we come in?"

"No," she hissed, "you'll have to wait."

But when Father was taken short that was one thing he couldn't do.

He stood up, excused himself and made half the row stand up to let him through.

He was still missing at the interval.

My sister said he might have got lost.

"I hope he *is*," Mother said.

I went looking but failed to find him.

Of course it's been greatly improved now but, in those days, there was a maze of passageways down which Father had blundered until he found a door that looked promising. He pushed it open and found himself out in King Street and, what was more, he couldn't get back in.

There was only one time when it came in useful and my old man used to tell that story with relish. It happened in the first war. He was a young soldier up in the lines, under fire. "It was occurd," he said, "but I couldn't wait." The Corporal had told him to lie low but, as the old man said: "I'd sooner be blown up than suffer in torment."

When he got back there was no trench, only a shell hole.

"Pity you weren't in it!" said Mother.

"Yes, but Alice, my dear," he would say, putting on his soothing voice, "then I should never have met you and married and had these lovely children."

There was no answer to that.

Above left: My old man in his Royal Artillery Bombardier's uniform, of which he was so proud. Above right: early in their marriage, Father and Mother outside Granfer's cottage. Below: My old man on his rambles, consulting the bus timetable on the wall of the pub at Winford

The Stonewaller

ETWEEN DOWNEND AND MOOREND there were, before the war, miles of fields with stone or wooden stiles, a newt-haunted pond, an area of heathland and an ancient Quakers' Burial Ground. This walk across to Moorend was a favourite of the family's on Sunday evenings. And, as always, Mother would trot out her memories of her grandfather, William, with a special pride.

"He made 'em all," she'd say, pointing at the dry stone walls that separated the fields, "with his own two hands."

Great-granfer Lewis had spent a great deal of his working life making and repairing these walls for the famous Farmer Bridgeman, who was a perfectionist and walked his farm every day to see that every wall, gate, hedge and field was being kept up properly. There was an old saying that Mother would repeat: "Farmer's foot fattens the land." That certainly applied to Farmer Bridgeman, who knew the condition of every crop, beast, boundary, workman and his family and was a churchwarden at Downend church.

What impressed Mother as a child was that great-granfer Lewis was so much a part of the scene. He knew every bird, animal and wildflower that he shared this bit of land with. And because he was abroad every day, without shelter, he knew what weather was coming up. According to Mother, he wasn't just an observer of nature, he was part of it. He rescued a nestling which had fallen from the nest or a nest that was threatened by the plough; he could imitate calls of lapwing, cuckoo, fox and stoat and had a deep and satisfying affection for them all.

When she was a girl of five or six, Mother's task was to take her granfer his "crust" or "vittals"—in other words his lunch of bread and cheese and onion with a bottle of cold tea. This meant finding him first. She would be told, "He's over the far end of ten-acre," or "You'll find him in the dippy by the spring, over past the hummocky ground."

And there she would find him, stooping over, selecting his stones buffeted by the weather, providing a home for mosses and sedums and ivy-leaved toadflax.

By that time, of course, he was old and bent. Rheumatics or arthritis, brought on by years of stooping and bending in the cold fields, had twisted his frame like the trunk of an old oak.

Seeing her, he would straighten as much as he could and chuckle "'Ere she comes. My little maid. Come and sit by the wall and talk whilst I eats me vittals."

She said once "Don't you get fed up, Granfer, with nothing to see and nobody to talk to?"

"Lar, bless me soul!" he cried, "there's plenty to see and hear; look, over there—this wall I'm mending have got little patches of hundreds-and-thousands on it. So I do put bits of root back in as I go. Over there I've been watching a throstle building her nest. She's watching us now. She do go and get twigs and bits of moss and then wait until she thinks I bain't watching and then she slips into the quickthorn like a flash. Just up over the rise, in the fuzz bushes, I see a linnet's nest with three eggs in it. I'll show 'ee, in a minute, as long as you do promise not to touch, 'n not tell anybody."

They'd sit there, old man and little girl, in the lee of the wall and he would munch his bread and cheese, slicing his onion with an old pen-knife because he had no teeth left.

Mother would ask him if he didn't get tired of always doing the same job.

"'Tis me task," he'd say solemnly. "'Tis what I's best at. Building walls is natural to me, like thatching and shoeing hosses is to others. My walls is good walls, though I says it myself as shouldn't. They'll last a hundred year."

"A hundred years, Granfer? We shall all be dead then."

"Yes, I count we shall. But I do make 'em for the future. After I'm dead and gone, people walking through these fields will say 'Whoever built these here walls, built 'em to last.'"

But they didn't last a hundred years. It seemed as though they would when I was young. I remember them and the way they followed the contours as though they had grown out of the ground.

Now they are all gone. Not one left. Great-granfer's life's work (and many another's) was bulldozed into oblivion when they built the housing estates at Downend, after the war.

A little valley, with a stream running through it, where the kingcups grew; the oddly-shaped piece of heathland where all the footpaths met and where the linnets nested; the Quakers' Burial Ground with its cluster of Scots pines—all have vanished under the tide of houses.

Was his, then, a wasted life? Were all his labours in vain? I think not. He helped maintain a pattern of life which survived long enough to be seen and experienced by his great-grandson. He brought up a family, in decency, with a respect for their environment and other people. And he seems to have conveyed, through my mother to me, a deep and enduring love of nature.

I never knew him but I remember his handiwork with pride. In my mind's eye I can see him, sitting down with a little girl in the lee of a stone wall, to eat his bread and cheese and watch a wild bird building a nest...

No Place Like Home

THEY HAD A LANGUAGE OF THEIR OWN with names which must once have been significant. But all too often the significance had been forgotten. Nobody could remember why they called old Mrs Gummer "Sullatch" or why Mr Howe was always called (behind his back, never to his face) "Buller" or why the Simpson family were always "Titlarks". The nickname wasn't applied to an *individual*. In this case, when Buller had a son he became Young Buller and Titlarks were—well, Titlarks.

Nobody seemed able to explain how they had come about in the first place. Maybe the connection was with the house or the land, maybe it had something to do with their family occupations, I don't know. Nor do I know why the Crown at Cockshot Hill is still the Shant or why that little group of cottages by the Post Office used to be known as No-Place-Like-Home.

"Where do *she* live?"

"Oh, she've come to live with young Quilla up No-Place-Like-Home."

To the small and silent freckle-faced boy in the shadow of the chimney corner these strange outlandish names evoked a world which haunts me still.

Mary-Anne lived in No-Place-Like-Home. She was a gossip and, not only that, she was the source of gossip in others; started rumours, invented stories which, because she was good at telling them, spread like wildfire, always prefixed with the personal disclaimer "According to Mary-Anne..."

Some of her stories were true.

If they had *all* been inventions she would soon have lost her credibility. But occasionally, even though outrageous, they would turn out to be true. Because of that she kept her audience and you couldn't help but wonder.

"She's at it again," Mary-Anne would begin. Her audience— she never lacked an audience—would wait agog to discover who "she" was and what "she" was at because, true or false, Mary-Anne's tales were always scandalous and therefore interesting.

"Met'n down the cemetery," she said, still chewing a bit of gristly meat from the dinner she had eaten an hour ago with a regular motion of her toothless gums. "Gettin' water for the flowers, you know. They met at the tap."

"Who did?"

"Why, she up at Tenacres. The one who lost her husband back in the summer. She with a brown coat."

"Oh, you mean Mrs Francombe?"

"Ah, thass she."

"Never. No. I can't believe it on her."

"But she's still in mourning," Alice Preddy said in a hushed voice.

Mary-Anne looked at them solemnly, her small black eyes unblinking.

"Well, do 'ee want to hear or no?"

"Go on," said Gran, intervening to save the story. "You've started it, let's hear what she's done."

"He was in mourning, same as she. Gave place to her at the tap, admired her flowers. Then he told her how he'd lost his and she told he how she'd lost hers and it ended up with 'em reading the inscriptions on each other's graves. He said he'd lost a gem, she said she'd lost a jewel."

At this point she stopped for another chew at the gristle.

"I just can't believe it," muttered Ivy Gibson, "and he not four months cold."

"You never saw 'em without they was hand in hand," bleated Alice Preddy. "Always together, hand in hand, even when they was only going down for a pint of stout at the bottle and jug."

"Cried for a week, solid, when he went," added Ivy. "Put ten lines of poetry in the Post to prove she loved him. Must'a cost her a fortune."

Mary-Anne went on smiling to herself and chewing the cud. She liked an incredulous chorus—it gave her story more dramatic effect.

"That was the first time, though; 'tis twice a week now. Tuesdays and Fridays. He brings his flowers and she hers and they... mingles 'em together." She said this with great meaning. It carried undertones that shocked Alice and Ivy into silence.

"Then they dresses the graves together, first hers and then his'n. But last week—"

"I can't believe it!" Ivy Gibson was still repeating as though the needle was stuck in the record, "and he only four months cold."

"Go on," Gran said, looking up from her stitching.

"Last week they went into the outhouse together."

"Not the one the gravedigger keeps his tools in?"

"That's he. And when they come out," Mary-Anne said with a sly look, "they was holding hands."

"Good Lard above!"

"In a holy place like that!"

"As sure as I'm sat here this minute on Mrs Wilshire's chair, watching her stitch that bit of blue cloth with this bit of gristle stuck in me stumps."

She demonstrated the fact about the gristle by removing it and throwing it on the fire. "Holding hands. And what's more, her neck-band, her black velvet neck-band what she wears in mourning of poor Sid who, as you know, caught his death delivering bread for Phillips' Bakery, when by rights he should ha' been home in bed... was all crooked... and they was red in the face."

Silence. Astonishment. Disbelief, mingled with pleasure.

"I'll say no more," concluded Mary-Anne, standing up and going to the door. "As you know, I'm not a gossip. But when I see a thing with *my own two eyes*..."

She left and, in her absence they wondered, analysed, recounted word for word—as Mary-Anne had known they would.

A month later, meeting, they compared notes. Mary-Anne was not present.

"Well, she was right."

"I couldn't believe it till I seen 'em together, thick as thieves."

"Holding hands—*in chapel*."

"Well, all I can say," Gran summed up philosophically, "is good luck to 'em."

"*Mrs Wilshire!*"

"They'm lonely, that's understandable. Both of 'em had happy marriages. They'll have somebody to talk to again. Somebody to tell how wonderful the first 'un was. After all, you can't go bottling it up with nobody to tell but yourself."

They "oh"d and "ah"d but they knew Gran was right. And when, in the course of time, Sid's widow was married down at Bethel, Mary-Anne was among the crowd round the ornamental gates.

"Told 'ee so," she said smugly as an aside when the happy bride arrived on foot—it was only a step from Bethel to Tenacres—in her blue-green morocaine dress that my gran had made special for her, Whitsuntide before last, and her black velvet neck-band.

Everybody nodded, submissively.

"But you wouldn't believe it," Mary-Anne kept on. "Thought it was just a tale, that I was making it up."

Everybody sighed.

She drew herself up (did I tell you she was long and skinny?) and pointed at the door of the chapel through which the elderly groom, complete with carnation, was now passing.

"Well, there's the proof of it."

They looked and it certainly was conclusive proof. They said they should have known, that they'd never really doubted her word, it was just that...

Turning away and smiling to herself because she knew that she could get away with six sheer inventions on the strength of this true one and promising herself that she would use them to pay off a few old scores, Mary-Anne returned to No-Place-Like-Home with a spring in her step.

Granfer's cottage (background). The cottage in the foreground was known as the haunted house. An old blacksmith lived there alone and could be seen at night moving round the house, eerie in the candlelight, looking for his wife who had died many years ago. According to my gran the poor woman had always yearned (in vain) for the bright lights of Bristol.

Trouble in Heaven

MY GRAN DIDN'T LIKE THUNDERSTORMS. Like many of her generation she closed the windows, opened the front and back doors, drew the curtains, hid the cutlery and crept into the little dark cupboard under the stairs.

"There's trouble up there," she'd say fearfully.

"What, in heaven?" I'd ask, thinking they never have trouble up there, surely!

"Ah," she'd say knowingly, taking off her spectacles and putting them in the drawer of her Singer sewing machine: "They'da have their troubles up there same as we do. You can't tell me the Good Lord sends thunder and lightning. 'Tis the Other One up to his tricks! He'da cut loose every now and then, see."

"Psha!" Granfer would scoff. "Old maids' talk! So long as you don't do anything silly you got nothing to fear, my son."

"How about Bill Brimble?" she'd say quietly, and that was enough to send him mumbling about his business.

"What d'you open the doors for, Gran, when you've closed all the windows?"

"In case he'da come down the chimbley," she explained.

"Who?"

"Why, the thunderbolt!" she'd say. "That's the way of 'em usually. Straight out o' the sky. Down the chimbley."

I had visions of a glistening silver bolt of lightning shooting down our big old chimney and blowing us to bits.

"They'm all right," she said mysteriously, "if you leaves the doors open." And, seeing my question, she answered: "Then they can get out."

In my mind I worked out what path the thunderbolt would take if it came down our chimney. It wasn't easy because it might choose one of two. If it went out by the front door it would cross the room via the rocking chair; if it chose the back door it would make a mess of our cottage piano, the Stag at Bay and anyone sitting in the chair by the clock.

"I see, by the paper, a thunderbolt struck a house on Siston Common yesterday," Gran would comment.

"That'd be Musty's," Granfer said. "He bin askin' for it for 'ears."

"Don't mean to say it was his house just because you don't like'n," Gran said.

"I'll bet ther a shillin'," he said. "No man can defy the laws of man and God and get away wi' it."

The fact was Mr Musty had done him in the eye over a sow with a litter some ten years before and Granfer seemed to think that, somehow, he had God in his pocket.

It turned out to be quite different actually. It wasn't Musty's. It was a cottage belonging to a decent old couple who'd never cheated anybody.

"There you are," said Gran. "I've told 'ee before, 'taint none of His doing. And you do owe me a shilling."

"Thees have to wait till I get the apple money," Granfer said. That meant never. He was a miser and never paid on bets, only received. "He set out to hit Musty's," Granfer confided in me, "but it's a bit too far to aim straight. He must'a missed."

"How about Bill Brimble?" my gran said smugly.

That shut him up.

There was something about the mention of this name that gave Granfer to pause. "Who was Bill Brimble?" I wanted to know.

"Nothin' to do wi' it!" Granfer grumbled.

Gran was happy to explain.

"Bill was a friend of your granfer's," she said. "Not a bad sort of chap. Real Christian. Went to church twice a' Sundays. Caretaker up at the school.

"Very conscientious he was, too. Always mending a window

or putting a hinge on a door. Thought nothing of thunder and lightning. Said 'twas for sinners to be frightened. 'Twas conscience he use' to say made 'em fear the thunderbolt.

"Well, the fence was broke down and he had to mend'n. His wife said to leave it for another day. Wait for the storm to pass over. But not he. 'D'ees think I'm afraid of a bit of thunder and lightning?' he says. 'Let they down the Crown quake in their shoes, I'll put a few nails in thik fence.'

"They were his last words on this earth. The pupils told how they looked out of the window and see'd 'n. Picked up a nail, lifted the hammer—and flash!... He was struck down dead as a doornail!"

"Might'a bin his heart," Granfer said grumpily. "There was a lot of heart trouble in that fambly."

"Dead as a doornail!" Gran said. "Proves to me that 'taint the wicked who need fear. Otherwise," she said triumphantly, "you wouldn' hear of churches being struck. It'd strike pubs. Yet you never hear of a pub bein' struck, not even the roof-tiles lifted."

"Old maids' talk," Granfer muttered, but it was noticeable that he didn't go hammering when there was lightning about.

As for me I joined Gran in the cupboard under the stairs. After all, if it could strike a man who went to church twice on Sundays, who was safe?

Left: Aunt Marshall outside her family home on Soundwell Road. She ran a dressmaking business in College Street in Bristol, (buried under what is now the Council House) and passed her trade on to my Gran (below)

A Golden Wedding Anniversary in the village for which I think my Gran made all the women's dresses. Gran is standing to the right of the table.

A Tree Full of Birds

THEY SAY THE WORLD'S DIVIDED into those who like trees and those who hate 'em.

I don't know…

Pagans believed trees had a personality, the Greeks believed in dryads and, coming down to modern times, D H Lawrence was a tree-worshipper. He said he could stare at a tree until he and the tree were one—feel the weight of its boughs, the roughness of its bark and the tree's awareness of wind and rain.

We had a lot of trees at my gran's. There was the bay tree by the front window. A blackbird used to nest in it every year.

There were apple and pear and plum trees in the orchard, a couple of gnarled old ash trees from whose giant heads Granfer cut his bean poles.

And then there was the Giant. *Our* tree in the lane.

It was actually on the side of the lane, a giant indeed, shadowing the land and part of the pigsties in summer and for us it was a tree of birds.

I haven't told you yet what kind of tree it was. When I tell you it was big and the trunk was as thick as an oak you won't credit that it was a hawthorn.

No hawthorn *I've* ever seen was anything like it. It was huge. Towered above our cottage, always a-twitter with birds. They seemed to come to it, as to a church. It was a sort of birds' cathedral.

Of course it was natural enough when the berries were ripe. The whole tree would be festooned in them. And you could hardly see them at times for birds—hundreds and thousands of birds. Gorging themselves on berries. It was as though it had a crop of birds rather than berries. Fluttering wings everywhere.

In spring it was a wonderful sight. May blossom turned it into a mountain of snow. Bees set up a buzz like a miniature power station. It changed with every wind and season: piling up leaves of red and gold on the lane in autumn winds, keeping wayfarers dry in sudden summer storms and threshing and plying when the winds of winter combed the whippy branches and set them streaming, like hair, against the racing clouds above.

When I asked Granfer why a hawthorn should have grown so big when, usually, they were small he said: "I kips me pig-manure up there. That must'a bin what got'n going. But a's getting too much on it. I sh'll ha' to have'n down."

"Oh, no, Granfer, you can't! He's... he's... well, one of us."

"'A might come down in a storm!" Granfer said. "Smash me pigsties to smithereens. More'n that, I reckon he'd just about reach the house. 'Tis a hazard."

Gran sided with me. She always did.

"You don't never hear o' hawthorn trees crashing down in storms," she said.

"Thass because there ain't none as big as he. He's too big for his usefulness, that tree. Don't carry no crop. Not a bit o' good."

"But he protects your apple trees," Gran said craftily. "Takes the wind off 'em."

"Ah well, thass true, my wench. But when I do hear the wind whipping up the branches into a frenzy, I thinks o' what might happen if he fell."

"P'raps he takes the frenzy out o' the storm," Gran suggested. "If it didn't whip the branches, it might have a go at our tiles..."

Granfer thought about it and decided to spare the tree. However, to satisfy his vanity he had to cut off two or three of the lower branches—just to show it who was boss!

It's no good looking for it now. There's no tree of birds—no cottage—no lane.

They knocked down the cottages, cut down the apple and plum trees, uprooted the hedges but they left our tree alone.

It stood there, surrounded by tarmac and semi-detached and all the splendour and beauty seemed to desert it. It wasn't covered with white blossom in spring any more, the red berries were few and the birds, finding their orchards and gardens replaced by roads and houses, flew away and never came back.

After the birds left, the big tree seemed to lose its vitality. It survived, but only just...

And then one night, in a high wind, it fell. It had weathered worse storms but it fell and it blocked the road for a while until a team of chaps from the Council came and cut it up.

Just as some of the old men and women couldn't fit into their new surroundings, the old tree must have known it was out of place. Without the deep green grass beneath and the other trees around it, it hadn't the will to live, I reckon.

So, when the wind came, it didn't resist any more. It slackened its hold and let the wind have its way.

Trees can't just get up and walk away, you see. They're rooted. All they can do to protest is die, give up the ghost.

Reckon I'll never see another tree like that. Not in this world...

If ever a tree deserved immortality, though, that hawthorn did. And it'll be there, of course. There must be trees in heaven. And birds. You can't tell me that things as good as trees and birds won't be there...

It was too splendid to be a victim of Time, that tree. I can see

it now, in my mind's eye—covered in scarlet berries and full of birds.

A tree full of birds.

Telling Tales

A GREAT TELLER OF TALES, MY OLD MAN, especially to children. I've known him stop kids crying and end up with a bunch of 'em standing round, listening, fascinated as though he was some sort of Pied Piper.

A favourite opening gambit was "How would you like a ride on my donkey?"

Or...

"Saw Father Christmas yesterday. He was asking me if I knew any boys who wanted an engine for Christmas."

In those days children really believed in Father Christmas.

He was out of work at the time, so he hadn't anything else but stories to give them.

"When's your birthday?" he'd ask a little girl who was crying because she had broken her doll. She'd stop crying and tell him and he'd solemnly promise that she should have a new doll as a birthday present.

Of course my sister and I knew they were only tales. We knew that all the time he was handing out promises the old man hadn't even the price of a packet of Woodbines—2d for 5.

Mother would say "Why do you promise kids things they know they won't get? Or, if they do, it's no thanks to you."

"I likes watching their faces," he said. "I like to see the light come back in their eyes."

"Hmph!" she said. "Think of the trouble their poor Mums and Dads have, making your tales come true."

He didn't tell *us* tales. Wouldn't have been much good. When the day came and the present didn't arrive we'd have made his life a misery. But the gipsy kids, over the Patch, believed every word...

You'd see him, leaning against a wall, with a crowd of

ragged, barefooted gipsy kids round him. "Next time I come this way," he'd be saying, "I'll bring my little donkey with me. Give 'ee a ride if you want one."

Well, of course, they all wanted a ride on his donkey and he'd solemnly take out a notebook and a stub of pencil and note down all the names of those who wanted a ride. Of course he didn't have a donkey. He didn't even like donkeys. But he could be very convincing, my old man. He could describe this donkey that he never had, right down to the colour of its eyelashes.

Next time he went that way he'd have another story to account for the fact that there was no donkey with him.

"Poor ol' Ginger," he'd say, "he's too poorly to bring out. Off his grub. I'm having to keep him in the stable."

And finally, if the children persisted, Ginger would have to die. He'd describe that in detail, too. Have these tough little urchins crying, tears making white runnels down black faces.

"Never mind!" he'd say. "I shall be getting a new one. Got me eye on a nice little brown and white mare. If I gets her, I'll bring her down."

The effect on his audience may have been gratifying to him, but it was embarrassing to us. We were always being pestered about the health of our non-existent donkeys or asked if we'd be with him on the footplate of the Flying Scotsman. Father, according to them, was its driver.

We never actually told them it was a bunch of lies: that he was lucky to get two days' work a week on the banana boat. But he went too far when he told the gipsies about Father Christmas. I suppose he lost his head a bit after his success with the donkeys. Anyway, it was very nearly the old man's undoing. They'd never heard about Father Christmas or, if they had, thought it was nothing to do with them,

Dad made full use of their ignorance.

Told them how he (Father Christmas, that is) had a factory making toys for children up at the North Pole. And on Christmas Eve he delivered them to all the children who hadn't been naughty.

"Shall we get any?" they asked.

"Depends on whether you bin good or not."

Well, of course, he was on safe ground here. They were a hardened bunch and, if receiving toys depended on being good it was obvious Father Christmas wouldn't be coming their way.

One little boy said: "What if we ain't been good so far but we'm good from now till Christmas?"

Father considered this with proper seriousness.

"Well, if you are—you'll get something. Mightn't be quite what you wants, but you'll get a present provided, o' course, that you got a chimney."

He went on to explain that, unlike the postman, you didn't need an address for Father Christmas. He came by air and delivered by chimney.

One day as Dad was walking up the lane he was confronted by three truculent gipsy fathers.

"We bin looking for you," they said. One of them had a cosh. They looked ugly.

"Oh ah!" said the old man taking a last long drag on his dog-end. "What about?"

"You bin tellin' our kids tales."

"No harm in stories."

"There is when we'm asking to build 'em bleedin' chimneys. We belts 'em round the earhole but back they comes 'We gotta have a chimney,' they says, 'or he won't come.' We told 'em straight that they won't be getting any toys. All they'll get is a leatherin' but they won't let it alone and it's all your fault."

"Now listen, you chaps," says Father, discarding his fag-end. "I got an idea, just you listen to me…" He was always at his best when he was in a tight spot. "Just you tell your wives,"—that was a laugh—*wives*—"just you tell your wives to use the old toy routine. When they're paying their visits for old clothes." He was too tactful to say they were out begging the Kind Ladies to give them their cast-off clothes. "At the same time they're asking for clothes," says Father, "they can be asking for any old toys because their children haven't got none for Christmas. They'll find it'll work like a charm."

And it did. They collected enough for their own kids and some left over to sell. And when the toys were found on Christmas morning, my old man's stock with the gipsy kids went up. They looked on him as a sort of prophet.

He should have gone easy after that but he didn't. He told them stories like they'd never heard before. About a magical baby born to a gipsy couple in an old barn. How three caravans followed a star and found the baby and worshipped him. His name was Jesus.

They'd never heard it and were deeply impressed. Especially with the stories of miracles. My old man told them how this Jesus was persecuted and starved in the wilderness and promised the people who believed in him everlasting life. He told them that Jesus gave away everything he had and told everyone else to do the same.

"That's one or two stories they won't forget in a hurry," he told us.

He was right. They took him at his word. Went back to the camp, collected all the things they'd pinched off other people and gave them back.

As you can imagine, this was right against all their parents held dear. There was hell to pay over there, across the Patch. Dad was warned that the men and womenfolk were out to get him and, if they did, they'd change the shape of his face.

"You've done it now, Gilbert," Mum said.

"I'll keep out of their way," Dad muttered. "For the next few months I'll steer clear of the Patch. I'll use Tripe Alley instead."

It would be nice to say that they were converted, but the fact is, I don't know. They departed soon after, during the night. Nobody knew where they'd gone, and we didn't particularly want to know.

The old man and my Mother at Selworthy in Devon.
It may look like just any old snap, but Ilford (the makers of film and photographic paper) asked for permission to buy the photograph and subsequently used it as a promotional poster.
And no, that's not one of my Father's tall tales.

My Friend Martha

MARTHA WAS A "CHARACTER".

There was no doubt about that. Even Granfer—who didn't usually approve of anyone or anything exceptional—had to admit that Martha was, as they say these days, *something else*.

She was extremely fat, lived in a one-roomed house beside the orchard and was a model mother. Granfer wasn't called Chooky for nothing. He'd known she was a wonder at first sight. That would have been at Bridgeyate market where he usually bought his pigs...

Oh, didn't you realise? Martha was a pig. A sow, to be precise and whilst other sows came and went in the three pigsties by the apple orchard, Martha remained. Although he had a reputation for being surly, especially to his neighbours, Granfer had a soft spot for Martha.

He would explain to me why she was so special whilst he scratched her back with a stick he kept for the purpose on top of the pigsty wall.

"That there sow, my son," he spoke slowly and deliberately, "that there sow is nearly human. What be I saying *nearly human*? She's a sight *more* human than a good many mothers in this parish. Ten to a litter," he said in reverential tones, "and not one of 'em neglected! Jus' watch her kip 'em in arder. And if one on 'em do soil the straw she da give'n what for, my lads! I never seen a sow like her. A masterpiece. A pig to be proud of."

To be absolutely honest I did not appreciate all her points at that time. Well, at the age of six one can't really be expected to understand the deep philosophy of pig-keeping. In fact it was several years before I made friends with Martha.

Then, at the age of eight, I discovered that, if I balanced

precariously on the top of a big stone outside her sty, I could just about reach her back with Granfer's stick. She watched my efforts with curiosity and when at last I was able to scratch her back with the end of Granfer's stick she closed her little piggy eyes and grunted in ecstasy. She liked to be scratched. Pigs do, you know.

Unfortunately Granfer's interest in pigs was not inherited by his children. Uncle Fred didn't care for their smell and my old man distrusted pigs, as he distrusted all animals . On the other hand my dad, who was a very humane man, never liked the idea of pigs being "cooped up" in their sties. On one never-to-be-forgotten occasion when Granfer was away for the day, my old man thought he'd give 'em a treat. So he opened the pigsty doors and let them out...

Talk about Gaderene swine! They rushed out of their sties like things possessed—running full tilt into apple trees, getting out into the lane and one of 'em got inside the house nearly frightening Gran to death.

After that Granfer had padlocks fitted. He went on reminding Father that his moment of weakness had cost him pounds in pigmeat for the next ten years.

"Thee father'll never make a pig man," he told me, in confidence. "He doesn't seem to understand their ways. No idea... none at all!"

A man who didn't understand pigs, in Granfer's eyes, was on the verge of being mentally deficient.

When I was nine I was allowed to feed Martha, once again in an interesting condition, but I could never reconcile myself to her diet. Granfer had ordained that this particular mixture of barley-meal and swill was a sort of magic elixir. It never had to be varied but to me it looked uninviting so I would sometimes add a toffee or a bit of Gran's cake. It seemed to me that Martha relished these additions. Particularly the toffees which she chewed up, paper and all.

Looking round for alternatives my gaze fell on the laden branches of elderberries near her sty. I pointed them out to Martha and she gave encouraging grunts so I fetched her some. She ate them with relish so I made a practice of mixing them in with her swill, turning it into a strange purplish colour. I can't claim to have invented anything here. For only the other day I came across a similar experiment by the famous naturalist W H Hudson. That was in Wiltshire, however, so it's unlikely his pig was related to Martha who was a Gloucester Old Spot.

Then one day he came out—Granfer, I mean—and saw what I was doing. You would have thought I had put his life in peril... "What bist doin'?" he demanded.

"It's elderberries," I explained.

"Elderberries? Pigs don't eat elderberries!"

"They do if they're given some," I said. "She likes 'em."

He looked down at me—he was a big man—and his eyes clouded with doubt. Not of himself or the sow but of my sanity...

"It don't make no odds," he said with the finality of a judgment, "whether she likes 'em or whether she don't. That's nothing to do wi' it. Thee cassn't feed pigs elderberries."

"Why not?" I asked, "if she likes..."

"Because," he said thunderously, "thee's might end up with purple streaks in thee bacon. And who do want bacon with purple streaks in it?"

Do you know I had never given a thought to Martha as potential bacon. For the first time I saw her *not* as a character, a personality, a perfect mother with a philosophy of her own and a liking to be scratched... I saw her as so-many-rashers-of-bacon in a grocer's shop. It was a terrible moment.

"It's not fair," I said, "after she's brought up all these families. To cut her up and have her for breakfast. It's not right."

Granfer shook his head at me and absent-mindedly scratched Martha's back with his stick.

"My son," he said, "I had high hopes for thee. I thought to meself, here's a feller who'll turn out to be a real pig-man like his granfer."

"But I *like* pigs," I muttered.

"Ah!" he said with a sigh. "You likes 'em to play with. But that ain't it, You got to understand 'em. Teach 'em. Feed 'em. Master 'em. And kill 'em."

"Why do they have to be killed?"

"Why, bless me soul, because they'm pigs. You don't want us to be round eatin' each other, do 'ee? Now, listen: you eats a bit of bacon for your breakfast. You enjoys it! Well, then... that's what it's all about. You wouldn' keep pigs in the first place if you wasn't going to eat or sell them afterwards."

"It don't seem fair," I mumbled.

Granfer grunted. He did sometimes—not like a pig but irritably.

"You bin listenin' to yer father," he said accusingly. "I tell 'ee, my son, you can't pay a hanimal a better compliment that to eat'n... no cause to shudder at me. 'Tis true. Only natural. When we eats something, and enjoys it, it becomes part of us. Thas's why we got to be careful what we eats. Every time we savours a piece of bacon we ought to be grateful to the pig what provided it. And the Good Lord who made the pig in the fust place.

"Yes," he said, looking down at Martha lovingly. "She'll cut up a treat, she will. A bit on the fat side. But I likes a bit of fat."

And, to my horror, he licked his lips.

Looking back I can see that of all the things I've failed at—and they are many—the list must include a pigman. I'd never have made a good pigman. I just don't seem to have that natural streak of realism that identifies friends in terms of bacon and chops.

The promised land beyond the sties: the long grass in the orchard concealed a world of fallen apples and other fruits—tantamount to piggy heaven! But after Father's ill-fated attempt to give the pigs their freedom, all this was definitely out of bounds.

The Voyage of the "Argo"

WHEN THERE IS TALK OF A GREAT VOYAGE—Ulysses, Francis Drake, Magellan, Francis Chichester, Thor Heyerdahl—I remember, fleetingly, the only unique voyage Ivor and I undertook. And it was not exactly successful.

It was Ivor's idea. He was a boy full of ideas. One week he was into opera—wildly excited about *Faust*—the next week it would be Shakespeare. We once rehearsed *The Merchant of Venice* in Gran's broom cupboard. Another time he was set on making our fortunes as industrialists making cigarettes out of fag-ends with Rizla cigarette papers on a cigarette machine which cost fourpence at Godd's in Market Square.

As I say, the voyage was one of these brief enthusiasms. And it arrived, with Ivor, out of the blue, one Saturday morning when we were ten.

"I know just the place," he said. "Candy's Pond."

Every village had a pond in those days, full of old bedsteads and newts and frogspawn at which the entire population of boys and girls congregated after a frost, in winter, to slide—we hadn't any skates—and toboggan above the newt-haunted depths far below the icy surface.

Candy's pond was not a very big one but, when it wasn't frozen, it was dangerously wide. We had tried once to cross it on a raft made of orange boxes but it hadn't been much of a success. I'd been dubious about it from the start. The raft looked terribly flimsy and I was doubtful if the tintacks (we couldn't find nails) would hold. So we experimented, in time-honoured fashion, by using Ivor's dog, Caesar, to make the maiden voyage. It was a good job dogs can swim or poor

Caesar would have sunk with the raft.

After that Candy's Pond remained inviolate for nearly a year. The newts were sought with fishing nets and the tadpoles with open hands but the centre of the pond was safe for amphibians. Until, that is, Ivor had this great idea...

"It's Candy's Pond," he said.

"We tried that with a raft."

"Ah yes, but we was younger then. We didn' understand. This time we shall sail across it, in a boat."

"A boat? We haven't got *a boat*."

"I've bin thinking," Ivor said, "and I know the perfect thing for a boat. In fact you might say it's a boat already. Sort of."

Having a naturally suspicious mind, even at the age of ten, I asked, "What is it?"

He glanced sideways at me to weigh up my reactions.

"Your mother's wash-tub," he said.

To say that I was taken aback would be putting it mildly. In our house the implements of cleaning were almost sacred. Her wash-tub, her scrubbing-board, the mangle and boiler were Mother's household goods. I could see Ivor's point. The wash-tub would make a wonderful boat—it  was wooden and roomy, the sharp edges had been smoothed by years of hard wear, but...

"We could drill a hole in the bottom for the mast," Ivor went on, "with your dad's brace and bit."

"Mother'd never forgive it," I said. "Drill a hole in her wash-tub? It'd be more than my life's worth. Anyway, why do we need a hole?"

"For the mast. I got it outside."

"Where d'you get 'n?"

"My mum had a brush on the end of it. I knocked it off with a chopper. We could make it fit the hole exactly and put sails on it."

"Yes, but what about when we've finished with it? What about the hole in our wash-tub?"

"Oh, that's all right. I got a cork in me pocket." He took it out and showed me. "That'll fit the hole. Nobody'll ever know."

No wonder he sold insurance later in life. Ivor could sell ideas to anybody except his mum and dad.

We carried the wash-tub down secret paths of the back field. I brought along the brace and bit and we drilled a hole in Mother's wash-tub for the mast.

Everything worked perfectly. The sails were an old sheet off Ivor's bed and the pole (to push off with) was my mum's prop from the clothes line. We decided to call it The Argonaut and I produced a stub of indelible pencil, licked it and wrote Argo until I came to the corner and the space ran out.

"It's ready for launching," said Ivor, so we set off.

Candy's Pond was in Mr Candy's field, reached through a gap in the hedge. Not a very big gap. If it *had* been, Mr Candy would have stopped it up. But it was big enough for small boys and it would have been big enough for our boat if it hadn't had a mast and sails.

We struggled to get the boat through the hedge, first this way, then that, until I told Ivor we'd never manage it.

"It'll never go through with the sail on."

"We could cut down the hedge," Ivor suggested.

"What with?"

"A saw?" he hazarded.

"Take hours and old Candy would come out and catch us."

There was nothing else to do but dismast the boat, insert the cork in the hole and settle for propulsion by prop.

When we'd continued to push the boat down the bank into the water I foresaw another difficulty.

"It floats all right, but how do we get into it?"

"I'll hold it steady with the prop," Ivor said, "and you jump down into it. Then you take the prop (I mean oar) and I'll jump."

This sounded like good advice but it didn't take into account the impact of a human body, even that of a small boy, on a wooden wash-tub.

I jumped and I landed in the boat, which then did extraordinary things—practically everything but turn over. Ivor did his best with the prop, I suppose, but it seemed to me that his wild jabbing actions were more likely to push me over the side than right the boat.

"Leave'n alone," I shouted. "Let it be. I think the cork's coming loose."

A trickle of water was seeping into the boat from the hole and I gave the cork a kick with my boot to push it in tighter.

That was a mistake. For two reasons: one was that Ivor chose this moment to come aboard, without warning, and the other was that the cork, receiving a hefty kick, went straight through the hole and out the other side. Ivor clutched me, I dived for the prop he'd thrown me, the boat bucketed like a mad thing and water poured in through the bottom.

"Row for the shore," shouted Ivor. There was always something heroic about him, even in defeat.

I pushed hard with the prop. It stuck in the mud at the bottom and the boat, which was now definitely a wash-tub, and a wash-tub with a hole in it, simply went glug-glug—and sank.

It wasn't deep enough to drown us. I suppose it came up to our waists but there's a sort of horror about immersion in muddy, frogspawn-filled water that makes it seems deeper than it actually is.

We thought for a moment our end had come and bawled for help.

Mr Candy must have heard because, by the time we realised we weren't drowned, only polluted, he was striding aggressively across the field with a stick in his hand advising us what he proposed to do to us.

We were horrible objects. Covered in mud and slime. Even Mr Candy was stopped in his tracks. His dog, Towser, stood still and barked whilst Ivor and I rushed for the hole in the hedge.

On the other side of it we looked at each other in dismay.

"You look awful!" Ivor said.

"So do you."

"What shall we say?"

"Tell the truth?" I suggested.

"They'd never believe us," Ivor said. "They never do."

"What about my mum's wash-tub?" I asked.

"We'll fish it when old Candy's gone in. We'll grapple for it." He was a very resourceful youth.

We explained our condition by saying we had fallen into a ditch. The hole in the wash-tub wasn't so easy. For some reason they thought I had done it and my tentative suggestion that it might be a knot hole was treated with contempt. I've never been much of a liar.

A Man of Property

NOT BY THE WILDEST STRETCH OF THE IMAGINATION could you have said that my dad was a white man. He had a very red weather-beaten face which had obviously endured more than its fair share of wind, sun and rain.

At the front of it—his face, I mean—he carried his nose, proudly, like the prow of a ship. It was an impressive organ and, when he blew it, the sound was like a liner coming into the docks. At the tip, it bent downward slightly so that, when his fag was down to the stub, you thought one more puff and he'll catch his snitch afire. But he didn't. Just at the crucial moment a deft flick of his tongue carried the stub from one side of his mouth to the other. It was the result of a lifetime's experience.

As I think I remarked before, his hat was his special pride, but he had a few more eccentricities of dress which I've never come across in anyone else.

He always had my gran sew a silk handkerchief onto the tail of his shirts. This extended the shirt-tail down to his knees and the old man used to tuck it up between his legs, like a Hindu, before he put his trousers on.

His trousers were specially made for him

by a bloke at Staple Hill. Very high at the back so that they nearly reached his shoulder blades. Braces, of course—he couldn't stand a belt—said it constricted his digestion. The high trousers were for protection—against the Atlantic storms that lashed Avonmouth docks, He worked on the docks more than forty years. Well-known for his voice.

He had a big voice. Quite extraordinary for such a small man. I reckon he'd bin given a voice a couple of sizes too large for him. In a crowd of arguing dockers you couldn't *see* Father, but you could hear him.

He had the voice of a giant.

Mind, his mates at work wouldn't have recognised him on a weekend. He was a different person. Carried a stock, wore a tweed jacket and, of course, his best hat.

He didn't need the stick to walk with. But Father wouldn't venture into the country without a stick. It was his defence against cows (he was never all that happy about livestock) and, of course, to gesture with.

He'd point out things which otherwise I might have missed— with a sort of... well, proprietary air! He had the look of a country squire. And you could tell, by the casual way he took his fag out of his mouth to comment on this and that, that he was a man of property.

Whatever he might do during the working week, Father was a gentleman when he "got away from it all". The fields and woods, lanes and streams were his inheritance.

He'd withdraw his fag and say: "Look at they birds' nests up there. Rooks. Right up at the top. Got a lovely view up there. But o' course, it's very exposed. All right for them because they never get dizzy, birds. Now if you or I was up there, we should be afraid to look down, but birds is different. They got wings, see. No need to fear heights when you got wings."

He was full of this homely philosophy, my old man. It irritated me sometimes because his knowledge of ornithology, botany and geology was absolutely nil. But he had a sense of wonder which, looking back, had a sort of wisdom about it.

Now I'll let you into a little secret. He had a private dream, my dad, that one day, somehow, he'd have a little place of his own, a cottage in the country, away from it all. He'd imagine himself, with his stick and his hat, strolling through his small estate, supervising this and that and keeping a benevolent eye on the inoffensive creatures of the wild...

Funny thing was, when he *did* inherit a cottage and orchards—Gran's—he didn't enjoy it at all.

Mother was all for moving in, doing it up, keeping a few hens. But the old man wasn't keen. He said he'd miss the street and the neighbours. He loved an audience. And, stuck in the country, he wouldn't have one. It was all right on a weekend but not as a full-time way of life.

"I'm thinking about you, my dear," he said. "You'd miss the conveniences. I should, too," he admitted. "Had enough of it, when I was a kid. Outside toilet, no proper heating, miles to a fish  and chip shop. Lovely to look at, when you'm passing by, but full of draughts and discomfort."

I couldn't understand why, now that he was a man of property in fact, he jibbed at taking it on.

"Ah well," he said, "you got to be born to it, really. Property, I mean. Not just a little place, down a lane. I don't call that property—when I talk about property," he said, exhaling

Woodbine smoke, "I means estates, farms, hundreds of acres. I should 'a bin born a man of property. I got the feeling for it. Buying and selling, letting it off, building a few houses for me workers. I don't call our mother's cottage property."

Mum had no patience for such moonshine.

"You'd never have done much with it if you had it," she said. "You'd'a frittered it away on fags."

"You don't understand," he said sadly, "they was me consolation."

"You could've had houses in the bank, Gilbert, if you'd never touched a Woodbine."

When she was out of the room he'd say "Your mother never really understood me aspirations. In a way she's held me back."

"Held you back?" I'd say. "How do you make that out?"

"She'd never let me speculate. You got to speculate, you know, to accumulate."

"You never had any money to speculate with," I said.

"No, well, I never. But she did. Saved it out o' the housekeeping. Spent it on furniture and that sort of stuff. If she'd let me have the handling of it, I'd'a done something with it."

This was sheer daydreaming because the only reason she saved was because she was a good housekeeper and she wouldn't have trusted Father with a penny of her hard-earned savings.

"Your father," she'd tell us, my sister and me, "is a born loser. If you was left with nothing between you and starvation but an old cow, he'd trade her for a bag of beans like Jack in the pantomime."

Overhearing, my old man said: "Turned out all right in the story, though, didn' it? They was magic beans."

"They wouldn' be if you got 'em," Mother said. "They'd be just beans. Kidney beans."

At times like this Father would retire within himself, puff dreamily at his fag and you'd know that he was far away, being a man of property.

And then, when he came into his bit of property, Gran's cottage, down the lane. But it wasn't what he wanted at all. There was always something to be done to it—the roof to be repaired, the chimney-stack was leaning, a wall was falling down, the hedge needed laying and the orchard was overgrown. It was hard work.

Not being a handyman, Father would view the thistles and crumbling walls with a dejected Woodbine. If he mentioned his troubles to Mum she said, "Well you always wanted to be a man of property. Now you know what it's like."

He'd take his hat off, briefly, and mop his head.

"Ah, you don't understand, Alice. Property's no good without capital. You needs the capital to get anything out of it."

"Well, if you packed in smoking you might have some capital."

He was trapped. A man of property without the desire to live in it or the capital to develop it. In the meantime it needed attention. There was always something. A new lavatory pan, the gate was broken, the drains were blocked... Father was relieved when he had an offer for it.

"I don't want to let it go," he said. "But there 'tis—you can't stand in the way of progress and it wants a lot done to it."

"If only you had been a handyman," Mother mourned.

He dismissed this idea with a puff of smoke.

"No good without capital," he repeated. "I can see why some of these big Lords can't keep up their estates. There's so much to be done all the time. Some of *them*," he said sorrowfully, "is short of capital."

So he sold the cottage and orchard down the lane and they came and knocked it down, cut down the trees and built new houses on it. For the first time in his life my old man had a bit of capital. But even that was a let-down. A responsibility. He put it in the bank, thought about investing it, changed his mind and decided to give it away.

As one of the recipients I asked him if he was sure of what he was doing. "Yes," he said. "I've gone over it, in me mind, and the truth is, I've lost the habit of spending. You can only *enjoy* money by spending it and then, when you've spent it, you're poor again. I've thought of a thousand things I could buy but it've come too late. 'Tis worrying me, so I'm getting shot of it.

"It'll be a load off me mind, actually. And when you gets older, you wants to shed burdens, not take on new 'uns. My father, now, he was a miser: he enjoyed just having the money, keeping it to hisself, but I keeps thinkin' what could be done with it. Like property, really. You thinks to yourself, how marvellous to be the owner of a great estate but when you comes down to it," he flicked his fag-end across his mouth with practised ease, "the pleasure of having it don't amount to much if you don't share it."

So he shared out the proceeds and he was neither a man of property nor a capitalist. He'd realised, by that time, that his real properties weren't bricks and mortar or acres of land but mansions in the mind, castles in the air. He saw them, in the cigarette smoke. And that was how he wanted to see them—fleetingly, beautifully, remotely—without having to pay the rates or mend the roof!

Old Shag and That

IF MY GRANFER WERE STILL ALIVE TODAY he'd say "I told 'ee so!" whenever cigarettes are described as a health hazard. He didn't hold with cigarettes. They were one of the many things Granfer didn't hold with... electricity and gas and labour-saving devices and even radio.

Granfer would never have the 'lectric in his cottage. Said it was dangerous. Gas was worse. And running water, in the way of taps and toilets, made the house damp...

Mind, he wasn't against smoking. *Proper* smoking. He liked his pipe of baccy—*Black Bell* it was called—and he smoked two ounces a week. Never more, never less. I used to be sent down Mrs Smith's shop to get it for him. He would give me precise instructions—what to ask for and not to accept a substitute and how much change there ought to be.

Mrs Smith's shop was in the front room of a cottage down the lane—sweets in rows of bottles, sherbet fountains, lucky bags, tiger nuts and, of course, tobacco and cigarettes. All these were available for cash but a large notice on the wall proclaimed that there was NO CREDIT.

You don't see sweet shops like that any more. You'd stand outside, with your nose pressed to the glass, deciding what sweets you were going to spend your ha'penny on and then you'd take a deep breath and open the door. It was a door of decision. And when you opened it the bell on a spring above it jangled violently. This was to let Mrs Smith know she had a customer. A timid person would have been tempted to take to his heels because that bell was like a fire alarm. It had to be. Mrs Smith was deaf.

If I was spending my ha'penny she would not have much patience, but if I was on an errand from Gran or Granfer it was different. More profitable, see.

"Ounce of *Black Bell*, please."

I think it cost about elevenpence then. A vast sum of money for a child to be entrusted with.

"Tell your granfer I'm out of *Black Bell*. I've got *Bishop's Blaze*, they say that's just as good."

"I better not. He says it's got to be *Black Bell*."

"Tell him it will be in tomorrow or Friday," she said witholding the gob-stopper you usually got free when you made a major purchase.

Granfer wasn't prepared to wait until Friday.

"I'd'a know she!" he growled, "'tis always coming in tomorrow with she. Thee's better go over Jimmy Honeyball's. He'll have *Black Bell*, I know. Smokes it hisself."

That meant I had to go across the main road. Jimmy and his wife kept the off-licence where things were usually a ha'penny dearer and there was no bonus by the way of gob-stoppers. The fact that Jimmy Honeyball was a character didn't compensate for the gob-stopper. And Jimmy wasn't my favourite character anyway. He was our local rat-catcher, boasted that he'd never worn an overcoat in his life. And he was never seen without his battered bowler hat on—people reckoned he must have slept in it.

What I didn't like about Jimmy was his way of giving everybody who came into the shop a nickname. Well it's all right if you're called Captain or Sonny but he used to pick on your peculiarities and I reckon it's rude.

"Why 'tis young Freckles," he said. "Whas's want? Penno'th o' spots? Ho ho ho!"

There was always a mate or two to echo his laughter, and the dog—he always kept especially noisy dogs—would bark derisively from a corner.

"How's thee granfer?" he'd ask. "How's his chest?"

"Not very good," I'd say.

"Ah," he'd say. "He've bin a martyr to that chest, your

granfer. I've knowed Fred Wilshire—what?—this fifty year," he said to his hanger-on, "and he's always bin troubled with his chest."

"P'raps 'tis the pigs," said Minnie. She was Jimmy's wife.

"No, you'm wrong there, missis, 'tain't the pigs, can't be. The smell of pig might get up thee nose but 'tis good for the chest. No, I reckon 'tis smoking all this stuff," pointing to the *Black Bell*.

Indignantly Minnie would say "Can't be for the amount he do smoke. One ounce in a month. That couldn' affect'n one way or t'other."

Jimmy winked broadly at his confederate, "Thee's mean he ain't bought but an ounce *here*, missis. Some people—traders—d'give children a sweet or two when they shops for their parents to encourage them to bring their custom."

"What! 'Tis bribery and corruption!" Minnie exploded. "I'd never stoop to do such a thing. 'Tain't fair trading."

Many years later, when I was eleven or twelve, I read the legend over the door of their shop and found, to my surprise, that their name was Hannibal, like that chap who crossed the Alps with elephants. It was quite a revelation. Everybody called their shop Honeyballs. James Hannibal—it was altogether different from Jimmy Honeyball—perhaps he was a descendant. By that time, though, James or Jimmy, who had never worn an overcoat in his life, had caught pneumonia and, in local parlance, was dead and buried in the fortnight. As a result, the rat-catching side of the business ended but Minnie carried on the shop until her eighties. In fact she might still be there if she hadn't dropped dead whilst running for a bus in Kingswood. Everybody said it was only to be expected, at her age—she would hve been eighty-six come Pancake Day.

However, as I was saying, before you got me talking about the Honeyballs, Granfer couldn't understand people smoking cigarettes. My old man smoked Woodbines and Granfer said he'd like to stuff 'em down his throat.

"Why cassn't smoke a pipe like a reasonable person?" Granfer used to tell him. "Not go roamin' round the parish with one o' *they* things droopin' from thee mouth."

"Any rate they don't make people cough like your old shag do," Father said defensively.

"It don't make *me* cough," Granfer said sharply, "And I don't smoke old shag. This is *Black Bell*. The best tobacco that's made."

One day when the spirit of enquiry was on me I asked Granfer "Why is smoking a pipe better than smoking fags, Granfer?"

He looked at me severely.

"A-cause it's more hijenic," he said, "and it's better for the garden."

"The garden?"

"Greenfly. Blackfly. Blight. Caterpillars. They don't like *Black Bell*. One puff and 'tis all up for 'em."

"H'mm, if it's as bad as that for greenfly I don't count it's very good for your chest," Gran said.

"What be talking about 'ooman! It's a well-known fact that tobacco, in a pipe, as 'tis meant to be smoked, kills germs. That's why Sir Walter Drake brought it back from 'Merica. That's why I spends me bit o' savings on it. I can feel it getting down there in me lungs, killing 'em off by the hundred."

After he'd gone out into the orchard, Gran said, "There, see—we bin married nearly fifty years and I never knew before what was wrong with his chest. 'Tis either blackfly or blight, I didn't like to ask which. Your granfer," she said sadly, "ain't got no sense of yewmour."

There's a Ghost by the Gate

I GREW UP IN A WORLD FULL OF GHOSTS. Mind you, they had a very good setting. There were owls in our orchard, bats in the old shed and ivy-covered ruins all over the place. Locally we had a collection of ghosts that made Jefferies' pond, the clump of trees up by Auntie Polly's and the deserted cottage by the conker tree notorious hauntings.

But the only place where I regularly saw a ghost was under our great may tree, by Granfer's Big Gate. It was always kept locked, that gate, and Granfer held the key.

When I used to come back down the lane of an evening from the New Buildings where Mum and Dad lived, I sensed presences everywhere. You've got to bear in mind the lane was pitch dark then and, if the moon was out, the queer shapes of misshapen ash and willow trees cast strange shadows. If there was a bit of a wind the shadows danced and the sight of a bat flying between myself and the moon didn't reassure me much either.

I was very imaginative at nine or ten and to me it was like going through the Valley of the Shadow in *Pilgrim's Progress*. I used to run all the way, reciting the 23rd Psalm. Somehow that protected me. As long as I could get that out, I was safe...

"The Lord is my shepherd," I quavered. "I shall want nothing."

Passing the Yeomans' privy and Dark Lane. Dreading the moment when I reached Granfer's Big Gate and gabbling, "He makes me to lie down in green pastures, he restoreth-my-soul..."

I'd put on an extra spurt when I got that far, because, over

there by the gate, out of the corner of my eye, I would see a wisp of smoke, a flutter of white. And my heart would be up in my throat, stopping me speaking, "Verily goodness and mercy shall follow me, all the days of my life, and I shall dwell in-the-house-of-the-Lord-for-ever."

"Whatever's the matter?" Gran would say. "You'm running as if all the devils in Hell was after 'ee."

One day I asked Granfer why he kept the gate locked.

"'Tain't locked all the time," he said. "I opens it up when they comes for the pigs."

That was true. When he'd fattened them up for bacon, a lorry would come up the lane. There would be a great squealing of pigs and shouting of men from the pigsties and then the lorry would drive off leaving the sties empty. It seemed a poor sort of end to animals who'd been almost members of the family.

"Has there ever been anything terrible happened there?" I asked. "By that Big Gate?"

"Whas's mean, terrible? I nearly broke me leg up by there once when the old sow turned on me."

"No, I mean human," I said.

Gran looked up from cutting the bread and butter (it was tea time) "There was young Mary Tyler, Fred. She lived down Tenacres."

"Hrmph," Granfer obviously didn't consider that relevant.

"What happened, Gran?"

"They found her up there, by that gate. After she'd," her voice sank to a whisper, "cut her throat."

"Silly girl," Granfer commented. "'Twasn't as if she was

goin' to have a babby or anythin'."

Gran nodded in my direction and they modulated their voices. It was something about this Mary Tyler being in love with a man who'd jilted her and married somebody else. Didn't make much sense to me. Gran thought it romantic and awful, Granfer thought she must have been weak in the head, there was a lot of it in that family.

They were surprised when I spoke up and said: "I've seen her."

"Who?"

"Mary Tyler."

"You couldn' have. She bin gone these twenty years. Before you was thought of."

I insisted that I'd seen her and that she was wearing a white dress.

This impressed Gran.

"She had a white dress on when they found her, Fred. All covered with blood, he was. They said she made'n herself. Her wedding dress."

Granfer snorted.

"Never heard such nonsense. Mary Tyler was a poor thing. Wouldn' say boo to a goose. Even if there were such things she'd never have the spirit to be a ghost."

After that I took to coming down Gran's by the long way, past Jefferies' pond, down Tripe Alley, past Aunt Polly's. It was longer and just as dark and I'd come in puffing and panting in a state of collapse.

When I told Gran about it she said it was dangerous coming past the pond, I might miss me way and fall in. If it was Mary Tyler's ghost I was worried about she'd have a word with Granfer, she said, see what he could do about it.

I didn't see what he *could* do but, a day or two after, he told me I needn't trouble about that old ghost any more, he'd cured it.

"She 'on't be there no more, my son. I've painted the gate with tar. Ghosts can't abide tar. Well known fact."

And he was right. When I passed the Big Gate that night there was no wisp of smoke, no flutter of a dress.

Next day Gran and I went and had a look at the gate. There, adhering to the tar, was a bit of material. Flowered. Bit of a dress. My gran, being the village dressmaker, knew whose it was. "That's Betty Coggins' dress," she said. "But what should it be doing here, stuck to our gate?"

Granfer laughed mirthlessly.

"Thee's better ask Betty Coggins," he said. "You'da know what they always used to call that gate when we was young— the Courting Gate."

"Not Betty Coggins," Gran said. "Her mother told me she don't have nothing to do with boys. She's a teacher down Sunday school."

"I don't care what she is," Granfer said, "thee wait and see."

A few days later Betty and her mother came in.

"Our Betty needs a new dress," Mrs Coggins said. "She's gone and mislaid that pretty flowered dress you made for her last Whitsun. Can't find'n anywhere."

With eyes on the floor, Betty said something about it being lost in the wash, but Mrs Coggins pooh-poohed the idea.

"You've put'n somewhere," she said, "and when you get another he'll turn up."

When they had gone, Gran said ,"Well, there goes your ghost, my son. Poor wench, she must'a bin frightened to death when she stuck to that gate."

"Ain't seen no more ghosts, have 'ee?" Granfer said later. "Not that I believe in 'em, mind," he added sternly. "I don't say as *some* don't see 'em... or think they do... comes of all this book-reading. I don't hold with it, half of it's a pack of lies. Except," he added, after a moment's thought, "the Good Book."

"Our Lewis reads that, too," Gran said.

He nodded approvingly. "Thas's right, my son. Only thee doosn't want to overdo it. There's some pretty queer stuff in there," he said grimly, "when thee's come to think on it."

Where My Lovely Caravan...

THERE WERE TWO DIFFERENT KINDS OF GIPSIES in our village before it was swallowed up by Bristol. Best known and best liked were the Loveridges, mother and son, who lived in a gaily painted caravan in a corner of a field by a pond.

Old Mrs Loveridge made paper flowers and told fortunes. Bob, her son, made and sold clothes pegs and brooms. They were part of our community. I remember when I was first invited into their caravan. It was like entering another world. Spotlessly clean. Full of interesting things. Copper jugs, brass bellows, hand painted china and an enormous Family Bible, bound in leather, with a silver clasp.

Neither of them could read or write. They hadn't the aptitude, they said. So the Bible was a symbol. And that was why I had been asked in. Although only a boy, I was known to write a good hand. And I was required to bring the Family Bible up to date with a couple of recent births and deaths in the special places provided—at the end of Revelations.

Outside in the meadow, which they rented from a farmer, their horse grazed peacefully. It wasn't used much. Just occasionally when they made their annual pilgrimage to the Romany meeting places. In a way that was a symbol, too.

Everybody liked the Loveridges. They were self-respecting, decent, useful folk. Not like our *other* gipsies across the Patch. Now *they* were a different kettle of fish: "Diddecoys", the Loveridges called them, and "tinkers". Unlike the Loveridges they never went to the annual meetings. In fact they never left their camp except to forage.

When, in the course of time, old Mrs Loveridge died, friends and relations came from all parts of the country. In their caravans, of course. It was a Great Occasion. We'd never seen such magnificence of flowers and coaches. It was like Royalty.

That left Bob Loveridge on his own. For a time he continued in the same old pattern. His caravan was as clean and neat as ever. He made and sold his brooms and clothes-pegs. And he kept up the old traditions. Then tragedy struck.

The field, in a corner of which the Loveridge caravan had always rested, was sold for "development". Bob was given his marching orders. He and his caravan and horse had to go.

The question was, *where?*

Solitary caravans in field-corners were a thing of the past. To be respectable you had to have a house, pay rates, conform or else move to a special site. Bob didn't fancy moving to a site. So there was only one thing to do. He wasn't short of money. They'd always been careful and in those days, of course, before inflation, the value of money remained constant. He bought a house. A great and terrible step for a Romany.

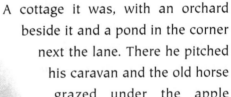

A cottage it was, with an orchard beside it and a pond in the corner next the lane. There he pitched his caravan and the old horse grazed under the apple trees. The cottage was used to store apples in. He lived in the caravan of course.

The cottage was to satisfy officialdom but Bob had always lived in a caravan and he didn't propose to alter his ways.

Things might have gone on like that for the rest of his life but there was a surprise waiting round the corner. I told you he was a bachelor, didn't I? Well, he was. And just as he'd got things sorted out he went and did a silly thing. He fell in love.

And she wasn't a gipsy.

Her name was Mary. She was good, solid, sensible—and, what was more important to Bob, quite pretty.

Their marriage wasn't a Romany wedding. It was very quiet. In our village church. And then it became a question of cottage or caravan. *She* would not sleep in the caravan. *He* wouldn't sleep in the cottage. In the end, of course, they compromised. And, as you would expect, the woman got the best of it.

During the week they lived and slept in the cottage. On weekends he went back to the caravan. And slept alone.

Then, one winter's evening—it was Bonfire Night, 5th November—we saw a magnificent bonfire. It reddened the eastern sky. So we went to see whose it was.

Outside their cottage, in the orchard, Bob and Mary were standing, silent, hand in hand, watching it burn.

It was the caravan. Going up in all its splendour of painted flowers and brass fittings. Burning like a torch.

We stopped and watched quietly for a minute or two before we slipped away—realising that this wasn't a celebration. Not just the end of an old caravan. It was a sacrifice. An old life for a new one.

Soon after, the old horse died and, not long after that, Bob and Mary had a son, the first of three. I waited and wondered and then, one day, as I was passing their cottage Bob summoned me in.

"I wonder if you can do a little job for me?" he asked.

"Where's Mary?"

"Oh, she's out at the moment. Down her mother's. Won't be back for two or three hours."

He got me to sit down and then, from a dark corner, brought out the old Family Bible. Placing it in front of me he handed me a slip of paper. On it were written the date of his mother's death, his marriage and the names and birthdays of his sons.

"I wonder if I can ask 'ee to enter it up?" he said.

Having done so, in my best copperplate, I asked him if Mary had written it down for him. No, he said proudly, he'd written it himself. Mary had taught him to read and write. Only he didn't think his writing was up to Bible standard.

Naturally I didn't ask why he hadn't asked Mary to record the family history. There was no need to. I could tell, by the way he produced the Book and hid it away afterwards.

This was his Past.

The one thing they didn't share.

With my first toy: a home-made wooden horse

My Old Man and the Party Spirit

MY OLD MAN WAS ALWAYS A GREAT ONE FOR PARTIES. You could always depend on him for telling a tale. It didn't matter much what sort of party—birthday, Christmas, wedding, funeral—he was seldom at a loss. Mother would try her best to discourage him: "Now listen, Gilbert," she'd warn him, "I won't be belittled."

He would promise faithfully he'd be quiet for once, as still as a mouse, but when the time came, and the excitement gripped him, he couldn't help it. "My old woman and me..." he'd begin... Mother hated to be called his or anybody's old woman but she had to smile and bear it, as my sister and I did. We didn't enjoy people laughing at us either but when my old man got his teeth into a story, the Last Trump wouldn't have stopped him.

Mind you, telling a tale can be useful. It was certainly useful when he was out of work and hard up, without even tuppence for a packet of Woodbines... "Come on, you kids," he'd say, "let's go for a walk". And we would walk up to Staple Hill or across to Soundwell, where we would always encounter a willing victim. If she was religious, he'd tell her about a vision he'd had, the night before last; if it was a tradesman who wanted a laugh, he'd have a story about some character on the docks; if it was a local politician, he'd talk about corruption in high places. If we were lucky, and the story was a good one, the victim would give my sister and me sixpence between us. It was always we who got the money. Father was above taking charity. After all, he had his principles.

As soon as we were round the nearest corner we'd have a share-out: tuppence to Dad for his Woodbines, tuppence for a bag of yesterday's cakes from the bakery and an ice-cream for my sister and me.

Of course there were no monetary rewards at parties. My old man's party pieces were a labour of love.

He had a face for it, mind. Mobile. He could pretend to be anybody. Well, almost enybody. He would be Billy Baber, the rag and bone man, who lived down the lane by Ball's Common and hadn't any teeth, or he would be the drunken Major leading them over the top in the Great War, with great bravery but in the wrong direction. He would imitate the parson or the chimney sweep and would invent as he went along. Mother would join in the laughter with the rest but, when we got outside, she'd put him through it.

"Anyone can tell where you came from," she'd say angrily—he was born and bred in Soundwell, once a mining area, without the benefit of farmer or squire. She had come from Downend which had a manor house and a squire and a rural background. Soundwell people, she once confided, were common. The church wasn't as big as the church at Downend and it had a cracked bell.

"The trouble with you, Gilbert," she'd say, "is that you tell people *everything*. You've got a mouth like the place you work." (He worked at Avonmouth when there was anything doing.) "When you told that story about our little upset over the furniture I could have died with shame. If you'd never told them they'd never have known we had it on the weekly and couldn't keep the payments up. I'd said I couldn't stand the colour and, besides, we daren't take a chance with it being green and Mother being so ill..." This was a reference to green being the colour of death. Mother was very superstitious. She would rattle away at him all the way home and he would be sheepish and apologetic because he'd exposed us to ridicule. Mother would say she'd never go to another party with him and my sister and I would say the same.

"It was only that it seemed a bit dead when we got there," he'd say. "Jus' thought I'd liven things up." That was his philosophy, livening things up; his mother, my gran, once told me that he'd been a lively baby and he went on livening things up for the next seventy years.

It was ironic that the old man's greatest party success was also his last. Aunt Lily's silver wedding, it was. She and Uncle Sid had survived over twenty years of quarrelling like dog and cat and Father was warned to be careful. "For heaven's sake, Gilbert, keep off family matters and politics," Mother warned him. "And don't mention trades unions."

Aunt Lily, Father's sister

Uncle Sid was a shop steward. So Father played it safe. He stuck to ghosts.

He had two or three quite good stories— all true, of course—and managed to work up quite an atmosphere. In fact we were at the stage where everybody's looking over his shoulder and jumping at every noise. The old man insisted on the curtains being left slightly apart—"So that if there's anything outside looking in at us we'll see it," he said.

At that point he excused himself in his usual polite way "Got to water the roses," he said. "Shan't be a sec."

But instead of going to the toilet he must have gone into a

bedroom, slipped off his coat and trousers and boots (he never wore shoes) and draped a white sheet over his head. He slipped out of the back door and moaned and looked in through the window...

"Oh, my dear Lard!" shrieked Aunt Anne "Look there, through thik window, 'tis the ghost of my poor Albert."

Everybody looked and shrieked and then, suddenly, the ghost vanished from sight and the sound of my old man's voice, upraised in anger and pain, came from the place where it had been.

"It's got Gilbert," Aunt Anne told us. Mother went white.

We sat there, petrified, for a moment or two, then Uncle Sid—I told you he was a shop steward—went cautiously to the door, opened it and peered out.

"Gilbert?" he asked tentatively.

"Course it's Gilbert," Father shouted testily. "I fell over that bloody gnome and I've broke me leg."

We carried him indoors with his shirt tails flapping in the night wind and his hand in place of a fig leaf and the more he groaned, the more they all laughed until he got into a temper and they laughed louder than ever.

That was the last straw but Mum, who was a Job's comforter, told him it served him right. He had Gone Too Far!

Horsey

IF YOU ARE OVER SIXTY YOU WILL REMEMBER THEM. Those odd, eccentric, extraordinary characters whose presence in our midst made life so much more interesting and dramatic.

They were not, like most of us nowadays, mass produced.

Some were gentry. Well, they could afford to be odd! Like the local squire, who spent all his waking hours on horseback and had the doors of his house widened so he could ride straight into his hall.

And that very shy old gentleman at Syston who never went out without his umbrella. Not because he expected rain. But, if he encountered a stranger, he would quickly put up his umbrella and hide behind it. It had a little window in it so he could peer out and know when the stranger had passed.

The middle classes were seldom so unconventional but the lower orders produced eccentrics in profusion.

Our milkman was one. His name is irrelevant because he was always known as Horsey, partly because he looked like one. We children used to follow his ancient horse and cart singing "Horsey, horsey, don't you stop, just let your heels go clippity-clop."

He didn't enjoy this humour and would flick his whip at us in disgust.

You might say Horsey was in business but it was a very small business.

He lived in a cottage down on the Common with a few sheds, three or four bony cows which he milked himself, and his horse, Lightning. A gruff and usually silent man, Horsey's life was dominated by horses. Not by Lightning, who was a poor old nag of twenty-three, but by the equine aristocracy of the race track. Horsey was a gambling man.

He had an encyclopaedic knowledge of bloodstock, form, trainers, owners and jockeys.

To those with an interest in the subject he was never without a fancy for the 2.30 at Sandown or the 3.15 at Lincoln.

You would see Lightning quietly cropping the grass at the side of a lane. Nearby, reading *Sporting Life* and marking up his fancies with a stub of pencil would be Horsey.

Between them they were his downfall. Lightning lost interest and died. So Horsey had to hump his milk around in two cans, one in each hand. He couldn't afford to replace Lightning because, in spite of his superb knowledge of the turf, he never had any money.

His temper worsened, his customers diminished until there was no living left. Horsey was done for. Or so we thought...

Next time we saw him it was not in the flesh. His picture was in the newspaper. Shaved. With a tie on!

He had won £1,000 in a football pool.

He was rich.

His former customers were not best pleased at this. They had supposed him dead, or in the workhouse. All that seemed to be his right and proper fate.

However they needn't have thought Horsey would disappoint them by becoming respectable. This was his big chance. He would prove to them that he knew his horseflesh by winning an even greater fortune.

He didn't, of course. He lost the lot. And the local paper duly recorded this fact, too.

Horsey was quoted as saying that he regretted nothing. He'd always wondered what it was like to be rich. Now he knew! He'd always wanted to place big bets. Well, he'd done that, too. "I've had it all," he said triumphantly, "and I've lost it. Who could ask for more?"

In a state of chronic euphoria Horsey picked up the gun he used for shooting rabbits, went out on to the Common and blew his brains out.

What a way to end. This was no common milkman. He had achieved the full status of a Failure with a capital F.

The Real Thing

O F ALL THE ROMANTICS I'VE EVER KNOWN, none were more inspired than Evie. She was a girl then. Eighteen. She read *Peg's Paper* and *The Red Letter* every week. She never missed a Ronald Coleman film. Her world was full of sunshine and roses and fascinating young men. The presence of a young man—any young man—would make her tremulous with apprehension.

It was a pity she was crippled. One leg wasn't too bad but the other was crooked and thin. She walked with crutches.

Her face wasn't pretty but it had a sort of likeable untidiness. Her body was square and anonymous. Her voice was eager and fresh as a child's and she had fine eyes. Sat in a chair, she didn't look bad but in motion she was a broken puppet; laughable, pathetic, undesirable.

She should have been hard and bitter but she wasn't. She was all softness and light.

When she talked about one of her heroes with eyes bright, voice trembling with emotion, I could understand what romantic love was all about. Which was strange, in a way, because I was only twelve, a boy, with a passion for football.

"He is dark and moody," she murmured, "not tall, not short, but manly. And he writes such lovely letters: 'My darling, I'm missing you. I can think of only you; your hands, your voice, your hair.' Oh, it's too wonderful, Mrs Wilshire. So thrilling, so—romantic!"

My granny who was a dressmaker, would twinkle at her over her spectacles.

"It sounds very good," she murmured.

She read romantic weeklies, too.

"And, in the film, they see each other through the window, from passing trains, going opposite ways: she rushes to her window and he to his, but it's too late. They are fated not to meet."

"Oh dear. It's not a sad ending, is it? I don't like sad endings."

"They know they'll never get the chance again. He reaches up for the communication cord in his train, she in hers. You see the trains stopping, hear screaming brakes, hissing steam—she tears open her door, he rushes towards her along the track and all the passengers are staring. They're laughing and crying, they meet and kiss. Oh, it's marvellous!"

"They'd have to pay £5 each," Gran would remind her.

"It's worth it!" Evie would cry. "Worth every penny!" She is still a romantic, thirty years later. Still crippled, a bit uglier, but her eyes still alight with romance, her voice is still young.

All the other girls of that time who were good-looking, slim and desirable, are middle-aged now. They have married and brought up families and they go to bingo. But Evie hasn't changed. I saw her at the library last week. She'd found a lovely book. "So romantic," she told me, it made her cry.

The funny thing is I don't feel sorry for her any more. She's a very lucky woman. She's never known The Real Thing.

Aunt Anne

SHE WASN'T REALLY MY AUNT. She was my granfer's half-sister. Older than he. Older, in fact, than anybody. Toothless. With long black skirts, thin white hair and button-up boots. And as skinny as a skeleton.

She came to tea at Gran's twice a week and, as I lived with my grandparents, I learned to expect her coming and hated it. I thought she was probably a witch. She looked like one. Her only enthusiasm was funerals.

"It were lo-ovely!" she'd croon. "The flowers! And three coaches, three! He might've been a lord! She done her best by him, I'll say that."

"But I thought they didn't get on?" Gran would say. "I thought they didn't speak."

"Ah, well, they'd bin married a long time," Aunt Anne mumbled. She didn't think much of marriage. She'd been a widow herself for nearly forty years and always gave the impression that her husband had died to spite her.

She would read all the cards on the wreaths, estimate their cost and then revert to less pleasant topics—the price of things, the wickedness of her neighbours and the latest news of the local sick.

"Mary-Anne can't live more'n few days," she'd say with relish. "Ain't passed nothing for a month. The hospital have told 'em to expect it any time."

My gran would try and ease her away from death and disease but Aunt Anne could be gloomy about anything.

"Our Lewis is doing well at school," Gran would say brightly.

"School! I don't hold with it. Fills their brains with foolishness, schools do."

"He can read all sorts of books."

"What do you want books for? 'Tis only a lot of lies."

The fact was Aunt Anne couldn't read or write. When I was ten I was writing letters for her to her son in Gloucester and her daughter in Tonypandy.

"Tell'er I'm having trouble with Preddy,"—that was her landlord—"he won't do the roof. Tell'er me legs have gone."

"She'll think you're dying," Gran would say.

"Let'er. I might be for all she cares."

When her children wrote back, Gran and I read their letters to her. They did not refer to *her* illnesses but contained much about their *own*.

When her sister Emma died she had *great* expectations. Alas Emma, who was much impressed by wealth, left her house and furniture to her son-in-law, who was well off. All she left Anne was her bible and her false teeth.

And they didn't fit. For a while Aunt Anne tried to persevere with them but they wouldn't stay in and every time she opened her mouth they chattered and fell to the floor.

It was a great diappointment.

Shortly after, at the age of 94, she cut a tooth. It was news. There was even a paragraph in the *News of the World*. This upset Anne, who never thought she would appear in a Sunday newspaper. What was more the tooth ached.

So Granfer, who had a workshop and always pulled his own teeth with a pair of pincers, offered to remove it. There was no National Health Service in those days and Anne was poor. He took her out to his workshop, brief silence and then there was a piercing scream.

Anne emerged clutching her jaw, blood everywhere.

"He's a butcher!" she yelled. "He've broke me jaw."

Granfer said it was worse than ringing a pig.

She never reached her hundred.

Despite the publicity of her tooth her passing went unrecorded and her funeral was one of the humblest ever seen in our parish. Two wreaths, three mourners and the coffin on a truck.

"Buried like a pauper," Granfer said sternly. "All her talk of hearses, coaches, flowers and tombstones—and look at it!"

"Poor Anne," mourned Gran. "All she had to leave was Emma's false teeth and she had left instructions that they were to be buried with her."

Granfer laughed, mirthlessly. "Huh! They didn't fit her when she was alive," he said, "and they bain't going to be much good to her where she's going."

He didn't particularise, but there wasn't much doubt. Wings on Aunt Anne would have been absurd. She was always cold in life. The best you could wish her, perhaps, was that she'd be warmer.

Moses' Ghost

"GHOSTS!" MY GRANFER USED TO EXCLAIM WITH DISGUST. "Ain't no such things."

Apart from ghosts, Granfer didn't believe in lots of things. Electricity, for instance. And cars, anything mechanical, radio and votes for women.

In his cottage the lighting was by oil lamp and candles, the WC was down the garden next to his workshop, which he called the Shop and in which, before the First World War, he and three or four others made heavy working boots by hand.

The lane outside was haunted at one time, so they said. Of course it was easy to believe in ghosts then. The lanes were lit only by moonlight and, when the moon was shining, it didn't really help. On either side the crooked old pollarded ash trees, with their enormous heads, threw weird shadows. If there was a wind blowing, in winter, their branches sighed and rustled.

Just the place for a ghost.

Our particular ghost was the severed head of a man called Moses. He had lived in the end cottage of the Batch and had cut his throat in the 1870s.

Granfer didn't believe it, of course. According to him Moses had always been a harmless old man when alive and would never want to scare folks after he was dead. He put it down to imagination or a couple too many pints of cider down the Crown.

"If I do see'n I'll find out what my double-bore do make of'n," he said.

Granfer was a great one for killing things. Unlike my gran, who wouldn't hurt a fly, he had enjoyed a bit of shooting in his younger days, killed his own pigs and made up for the absence of a vet or the RSPCA by drowning unwanted kittens for tuppence a head.

I remember a mouse-trap we had which caught mice alive, in a little cage. Granfer was all for giving it to the cat but Gran said it was cruel and wanted to release it.

"Not in my house," he said. "If you'm so soft-hearted go and let the little beggar out into Buller's orchut." Buller Howe was his bitterest enemy. "He got plenty of mice a'ready so one more won't make no difference.

To come back to ghosts.

One evening our neighbour, Mrs Haycock, came running in. "I've seed'n," she said. "I dursn't go up home. 'Twas Moses' head. I shall see it in me dreams. All white and deathly with great staring eyes."

Granfer took down his double-bore shotgun, loaded, and went out into the lane.

He was gone for hours. Watching and waiting whilst the evening got later and the wind colder.

Then he saw something that made the hair on his head rise.

A great white head floated towards him, crying out like a soul in anguish. Granfer aimed at the staring eyes and fired.

"Well," he said later, holding it up, "there's your ghost, missis."

It was an enormous white owl.

He had it stuffed and put in a glass case to prove his point, and when I was a child it resided in my bedroom.

It may not have been a ghost but it certainly haunted my dreams.

What's in a Name?

DID I TELL YOU MY OLD MAN WAS A CHARACTER? Well, he was. So was *his* father, my grandfather. According to Granfer, his father, old Isaac Wilshire was pretty eccentric, too. He had a long white beard which was his pride and joy. Every day he washed, combed, brushed and oiled it: a ritual which took the best part of an hour. Gran told me he looked the living spit of Old Father Time when he was cutting the orchard grass with his scythe.

They were all very different. Old Isaac was a tyrant, apparently, and it was he who started the Workshop, down the garden, in which they used to make boots. Or, at any rate, parts of them. They were outworkers for the factories and, every week, had to take the boots they'd made and collect leather for the new ones from Croot's. Though they were very different, my granfer was a tyrant, too. He was a big man. Nearly twenty stone and six feet tall. He had a big voice, too, when it was upraised. If he caught the local boys raiding his orchard or breaking his hedges you could hear his bellow half a mile away. Gran said he had a bellow like the "bull of Bashem".

As an old man, Isaac acquired quite a reputation as a herbalist. Apart from distilling elderflower water (for stomach upsets) he made up medicines and rolled pills. Granfer said the pills were as big as marbles and hard to swallow. He seldom referred to his father and certainly had no confidence in his remedies. The book in which old Isaac had written down his lore was thrown on the back of the fire and the only trace that remained of his art were the herbs which still grew round our cottage. There were pellitory-of-the-wall, coltsfoot, mallow, marjoram, boyslove, sage, thyme and rosemary. There was also an old bay tree in which a blackbird nested. Although Granfer hadn't been Isaac's favourite—as my father wasn't *his* favourite— he had inherited the cottage and orchard. It was a long story and I haven't time to tell it but, anyway, he inherited it, herbs and all.

As for the Workshop, Granfer carried it on for a time until the machines took over and then he retired. He didn't approve of machines. In fact there wasn't very much he did approve of: he disliked cars and aeroplanes, gas and electricity, females and foreigners. In his cottage there were oil lamps and the toilet was relegated to what he considered its proper place—up the garden.

Granfer had to wait until he was seventy until he qualified for a pension. That was because he had been self-employed and you couldn't claim it at sixty-five unless you had paid National Insurance. Granfer didn't approve of insurance.

When his seventieth birthday came, Gran said "Now you can get your pension, Fred." He agreed to apply but you had to send your birth certificate or a copy of the parish register, and that was awkward because Granfer never had a birth certificate.

"That's all right," my uncle said, "we'll write to Somerset House. They'll have the record." But they didn't. According to their records nobody by the name of Fred Wilshire had been born on September 25th, 1856.

Granfer was flabbergasted. He had been looking forward to that ten shillings a week. It would make all the difference when he had to find money for the rates and his bit of baccy. His income from keeping a few pigs and the sale of apples threw a great burden on Gran, who slaved away, early and late, dressmaking.

Next thing was to consult the parish register. Our parish was Downend, but in 1856 Downend came under Mangotsfield. There was no entry in the registers there. And then, when we were all at our wits end, his elder sister, my Aunt Anne, remembered that he hadn't been christened at Mangotsfield but at Bitton, four miles away.

"Just like my father and mother to be occurd," Granfer said. "Just because they didn't agree with the vicar they had to take their poor little babby right over to Bitton. I tell 'ee, he had no feeling, my father."

Well, we looked up the parish register at Bitton and there, sure enough, it was. Father: Isaac Wilshire, bootmaker, of Soundwell; Mother: Deborah, his wife. Child's name: Joseph.

Joseph!

Granfer refused to believe it. No, he said, he wasn't going to have it. His name was Fred. It had always been Fred, he'd been married as Fred, Everybody knew him as Fred. "I don't even like the name of Joseph," he said bitterly. "It do make me sound foolish. No, they can kip their pension. I'll do wi'out it. Never mind about the baccy, I'm staying Fred no matter what they do say."

Aunt Anne didn't improve things when she was told.

"Joseph, that's right, that's what it was. 'Twas Mother's idea. She wanted thee named after that chap who did so well in Egypt. And then, after 'twas over and they got home, Father said he didn't care for the name and he thought he'd call you Fred."

"Well, why cussn't say so before?" Granfer demanded.

"I never thought on it. 'Twas so long ago, Fred—I mean Joe."

"Don't call me by that name. I don't want it mentioned ever again. It ain't to go beyond these four walls."

Here lieth the Body of

Fred Wilshire

Died

He produced the family bible in which all the births, deaths and marriages were recorded and made everyone present swear they wouldn't tell.

However, my gran made a mental reservation when she swore. She intended they should get that pension and she wrote off to the Postmaster General up in London and explained the whole thing. She told him that my granfer would never sign in the name of Joseph if it meant a thousand pound. And, I must say, the man was very understanding. He wrote back and said that, in this case, my granfer would be registered as F Wilshire and he could sign his pension book to that effect. Which he did.

Now, you may think I'm breaking my oath by telling you this. But, you see, I was only a kid at the time and they thought I was too young to swear.

Anyway Granfer lived and died—at the age of 84—Fred Wilshire. And, if you want proof, just look and see for yourself if you visit Downend churchyard. Fred Wilshire. There it is, for all to see. Carved in stone.

Three generations of the family: My sister Stella, Granfer, Gran, me and Mother in Granfer's orchard. My father, of course, is on the other side of the lens.

Ikey

YOU DON'T MEET CHARACTERS LIKE IKEY NOW. He was an oddity fifty years ago. One on his own. Nowadays he'd be locked up.

On a shabby old cart pulled by Peggy, his ageing mare, were the words ISAAC HOBBS—GENERAL DEALER. This was Ikey's dignity, his achievement, his life.

As a boy he'd never been allowed to play with other boys. As a man, he'd never gone out to work like other men. He was self-employed. A General Dealer.

His cottage was old and overgrown with ivy. Ikey's wife had tried to civilise him but given up. In the gaping barns and mouldering sheds he kept fowls, pigeons, a billy-goat and Peggy, the horse. She, like the billy-goat, was always escaping through Ikey's unruly hawthorn hedges so that when you saw the old man he was always looking for horse or goat.

Apart from pursuing his animals you seldom saw Ikey in daytime. Like the stars, he came out at night. Then you'd see him, with his grey hair and seamed face, sitting up behind Peggy, with a sack over his shoulders and a pile of junk on the cart.

His only real daytime activity was at market. There he would be seen among the bedsteads, broken bicycles, rolls of rusty wire netting and pictures of the Stag at Bay. His barns were full of such things. I remember seeing a huge pile of army boots, left foot, size tens and asking him what he wanted them for.

"Bought 'em cheap," he sniggered.

"Yes," I said dubiously (I was ten), "but they're all for the left foot. They aren't pairs."

"Ah," he said artfully, "thass why I got 'em cheap, see."

"But what'll you do with them?"

He winked.

"It's the leather," he whispered. "Lovely bit of leather. Worth a fortune."

My cottage bedroom overlooked his orchard and, when I was in bed, sometimes I'd watch him picking apples with the help of a lantern and a full moon. He had a theory that fruit should be picked at night. It kept longer.

To him apple growing wasn't just gardening. It was a form of magic. You didn't just plant a tree, you had to wait for a sign. With the hole dug and the tree ready you waited for a moon that was waxing, not waning, and the arrival of a corpse.

It might be a dog or a cat, a pig or even—some people said—an unwanted baby. But you needed a body to get the tree going. And, of course, it had to be planted at night.

When Ikey's time came he died at night. And I'm sure he would have wished to be buried at night, at the bottom of an apple tree.

His widow was no pagan, however, and, after she had disposed of his "bargains" and left-footed boots to the dustmen, she had Ikey buried in the cemetery, along with normal people, without mystery or magic and according to the rites of the church he had visited only twice in his life. And once afterwards.

Ikey's cottage was behind the trees on the left

The Last Nobbin

"POOR OLD BILLY," MY OLD MAN WOULD SAY, "he've hit a rough patch. We shall have to get a nobbin up for him."

"What, *another* nobbin?" Mother said. "That's the second this month."

Mother didn't go much on nobbins. She didn't like the word—it had a strange, crude tang of work about it—Father's work—on the Docks. Like so much of that rough, masculine world it sounded... uncouth. *Nobbin.*

We gathered that, when a workmate was down on his luck, in poor health, couldn't keep up the instalments, lost his wife or fell foul of the Law—the answer was a nobbin. Somebody got up a nobbin for him—made a collection, passed round the hat. It must have been a godsend because, of course, dock work was casual labour then. If you didn't work you didn't get paid. Still, not all the nobbins proposed were approved of—or as they would say "jonick". A sort of committee of elder statesmen made the final decision. My old man was prominent in these discussions. I can hear him now...

"Jack Boyle come up to me about a nobbin for Jackson. I told'n straight. 'He had one last year,' I sez, 'and the year before that. Nobbins don't grow on trees, my son.' 'Tain't like an annual subscription. I don't doubt but what the man's bad. He bin bad, on and off, ever since I knew him. But, blimey, there's a limit. He've had two nobbins an' that's his lot. What I sez is if he's goin' to snuff it, let'n get on with it and we'll send a wreath, but all this business about not-expected-to-live and then he goes and gets better ain't jonick."

Mother wasn't so sure.

"He can't help it if he gets better." she said.

"We don't never have THREE nobbins," Father said

doggedly. "Anyway, I don't suppose I shall ever get one myself."

"Let's hope you never need one," Mother said, but the thought played on his mind.

"That'd be typical," he said. "After getting up nobbins for everybody else for twenty years, I don't s'pose anybody'd bother to get one for me. The trouble is, see, these young chaps who're coming on don't see the sense of it. An' the old 'uns have all took their nobbins and retired. When it comes my turn to meet with trouble or drop dead or summat they'll say 'Gilb Wilshire—never heard of 'n!'"

"Well, it's you own fault, Gilbert," Mother said. "You will get involved. I've always told you to keep your nose out of it, but you will get involved."

This was a sore point and I'll tell you why. My old man had a real Wilshire nose. A bit on the big side—like mine. A sign of character, he always said, but I knew he didn't like being teased about it. Well, you don't, do you? After all you can disguise almost everything else: false teeth, a bit of padding, a wig. But there's not much to be done about a big nose...

However, to get back to nobbins, I remember Father coming

home from work one day and saying he didn't have time for tea, had to wash and change and go out again. Up to Hatfield to visit a mate of his who had been home ill. Apparently, when he hadn't come in to work for two weeks, Father had made a nobbin and sent it to him but had had no reply. As Father said, apart from not knowing whether he'd received it or not, the man might be dead and buried for all they knew.

"I've got to put me mind at rest," the old man explained. "It's a tanner on the buses but I owe it to the blokes who donated."

Mother wanted to know why.

"Matter o' principle," he said. When things were a matter of principle there was no more to be said. That wouldn't have mattered so much if Father hadn't had so many of them. He had as many principles as a hedgehog has fleas.

He was gone for several hours then returned with a face like thunder.

"What's the matter, Gilbert?" Mother asked. She could tell there was something wrong. "Is it the buses?"

"No," he said.

"How was he—the man you went to see?"

"Never mention that name in this house!" said Father.

"I can't," she said. "I don't know what it is. All I know is you were going to see him about this nobbin…"

"Don't mention that word, either. Nobbins. I've made hundreds of 'em, but never again. Never again."

It wasn't until he eaten his tea and subsided into a chair that Father recovered his composure. Then he told us what had happened.

"As you can bear witness," he said, "I didn't even stop for tea. I was worried about 'n. Not hearing from the man I had to find out whether he received it all right. Besides, the blokes kept asking how he was getting on and I felt stupid when I had to say I didn't know."

"Naturally," said Mother. "You would."

"So I went. Up to Hatfield. Two buses each way. And, even then, I had to ask any number of people where the road was. It's sickening how ignorant some people are about the place they live in."

"How was he?"

"Oh, *he* was all right. Nothing wrong with him. Fit as a fiddle. Just bought a bleedin' new car."

"I thought he was off with a rupture?" Mother said.

"Ah…" said the old man, bitterly, "he's played on that for years. Whenever there was a heavy job to do it was always 'You men know I would if I could but I've got to think of my hernia.' We wasn't allowed to forget about his bloody hernia. When I knocks on the door he answers it, in person. Dressed up like a toff. 'Oh Gilbert,' he sez. 'Come on in. Sit you down. Have a glass of sherry just to celebrate my good fortune.' 'What good fortune?' I asks. 'Ho,' sez he, 'didn't you know? I come up on the pools. Of course I can't tell you how much. It's a secret. But we shall be moving out of this neighbourhood. And you won't see me on the docks any more'. Alice, you could've knocked me down with a sledge-hammer. 'How about the nobbin?' I asked. 'Oh, yes,' sez he, 'it was a very kind thought on your part. Not as much as I might have expected considering all my service, but it's the thought that counts, isn't it?'"

"Did you get it back?" Mother asked.

"No, I didn't. I ask'n why he didn't send it back or reply and he said he hadn't had much time to write and it didn't seem right to send it back after it was collected for him. What got my gall was that he said that it might be best if I didn't mention his—good fortune. If they knew, some of 'em might be after it, he said. Better to tell 'em he'd had a nasty operation and wouldn't be back. I told'n what I thought about that and I left... I shall tell 'em the truth," Father said.

"Won't they think they ought to have their contributions back?"

Mother was always practical.

"I don't care," the old man said wildly. "I don't care if I've got to pay 'em back meself."

"Don't talk silly, Gilbert. You haven't got five pounds. And why should you? I know, I know," she said, seeing the look on his face, "it's a matter of principle, but your principles come expensive."

That was Father's last nobbin. He never organised another and when I asked him the name of the chap he'd called on, he showed his feelings by spitting in the fire. "Jack," said the old man. "That's his name. I'm-all-right-Jack. Cost me a ruddy fortune in bus fares and all I got from the men was abuse."

"You'll get over it," Mother said and, of course, he did. He recovered most of his principles but never got up another nobbin.

Father and Mother on a day out at Tintern Abbey

Farmer's Nanny

"YER, I BET THEE'S NEVER SIN ONE LIKE HE!" he would begin, taking some object wrapped in dirty newspaper from his pocket.

It could be anything: a potato shaped like a private piece of anatomy, a carrot with three tails or an apple with a baby on its back...

"Whas's think uv 'e then?"

If you didn't know better you might suppose that everything Farmer grew was misshapen, fantastic—improper. He himself was rather peculiar. He looked like a product of the soil—as though he had grown out of it, though there were old people round about who said he'd had a mother and a father in his young days like anybody else.

Everybody called him "Farmer" and the name somehow fitted him. He wasn't a farmer, of course. You couldn't even call it a small-holding, it was just a large garden, near on an acre, on which he grew veg and fruit, forced rhubarb—and played host to his friends in a bit of a shed.

Much of the activity centred round what Farmer called his Greenhouse—the most rickety, propped-up, casual affair you ever saw. He'd made it himself out of bits of wood left over on a building site. Many of the panes of glass were cracked and not a few missing altogether, being replaced by pieces of cardboard or advertising signs—Reckitts Blue, Fry's Cocoa, Colman's Mustard.

Few people dared risk entering this place, however. It shook and rattled in the slightest wind and a bad storm would bring down a shower of glass. That was why the weather forecasts always came first in Farmer's apprehensions...

"These-yer sou'westers," he'd say. "They'm a curse to me, in my line o' bisness. They'm like as not to bring me hool green'ouse down about me ears. I got to be on hand, day'n night. Ready to shoor'n up, s'know, in case of a mighty gert blast."

His language was as broad as his face. When he said "shoor" it up, he meant *shore*, and when boys made a gap in his hedge it was a "shoord", a throwable stone was a "quinnut" and a cut was a "scrage". There was also a great deal of "thee bist" and "tha ootn't" and I could never really understand why a horse was a "hoss" and hospital the "harspittal".

I once asked him if he ever listened to the radio but he told me, no, his wife had'n on but 'twas too much like hard work listenin' to 'em.

"My missis do say to I: 'Come and listen to the News,' but I d'tell 'er 'When 'tis somethin' consarnin' we, I ool. But don't ask I to puzzle me brains wi' all that uplandish jibberish about foreign parts'. Most all of it," he explained, "is to do with places thee's never heard on and fellers thee oosn't have a drink wi'."

Farmer's preference was for a yarn with a friend in his hut. This was not as shaky as his greenhouse and it had the luxury of a few broken chairs for company.

"Giss a fag," he'd say, "and I'll tell thee a story. 'Tis true, mind—I ain't clever enough to make 'em up."

They were usually worth a fag and although I smoke a pipe myself, I always carried a packet for bribes. The story I remember was about his Nanny. She was one of the other characters in our community. She was, of course, a goat...

"Young Carter says to me, he says, 'Farmer, I got a problem. The grass in me archut,' he says, 'do graw sa vast I can't kip it down. 'Tis too much for a lawn mower an' not anuff to make hay wi'. Whas's reckon I ought to do wi' it?'"

I ought to explain that "Young" Carter, a man of means, with his own business, was in his fifties. For a certainty he wouldn't have used Farmer's dialect but, allowing for that, the tale could well be true.

"I said to'n 'Thee's wanna get a kid,' I says.

"'Naw, not I,' says he. 'Now I've got 'em off me hands, I don't want'a start that again.'

"Sire, I couldn' help but laugh. I told'n, I said 'When I d'say a kid, I'm usin' the word proper. A young goat, thas's what thee wants ! Not *too* young, mind. No good getting one as ain't bin weaned. Just as it happens I got the very thing for 'ee— pretty as a picture he is. Bred out a' my nanny. Jus' the right age. White as the dribben snow. And, though I says it as shouldn', that kid was a credit to 'er. Gert eyes on 'en and a sart uv perpetual smile. I'll let thee haven' for a quid,' I says, and he paid up like a toff.

"'What do I feed'n on?' he asks and I told'n what the' was to give'n. Apart from the grass, of course.

"Well, so he takes this little kid of nanny's and lets'n loose in his archut. But you know what 'tis wi' goats. They'm wanderers. If there's a shoord as big as a tea-cup, they'll be droo'n. Carter, he was forever tailing after thik goat.

"'He've escaped again, Farmer,' he'd cry. 'Only lef' the gate on the jar for a minute and he was off like a long-dog.'

"Trouble was he din't care where he went or what he et. Carter was always payin' out for this-that-an'-tother... a bed of gladiolies, two rows of shallots, eben a clo'es line o' ladies' thee's-know-whats.

"'Thik goat'll eat me out o' house 'n home,' moans Carter. 'Ah but he kips the grass down,' I told'n. 'Thee cassn't grumble about that.'

"'If only he'd stick to grass I shouldn' have no worry,' says he, but I told'n goats is like that. Try anything oncet.

"He stuck it fer about a year and then he comes to me an' he says, 'Farmer, I give 'ee a quid fer that goat. Now I'll give thee another quid to take'n off me hands.'

"'Ah, well,' I says, 'I'd like to oblige 'ee, my son, but I got no use for a Billy at present. Whas's the matter, Mr Carter, is her too upstropolous fer 'ee or is it the smell?' 'Well, I must admit,' young Carter says 'the smell *is* rather... overpowering. We didn' notice it at fust but it've got wuss, Farmer, till it do seem to seep into everythin'... Not only out in the garding. It seems to be getting into the house now. Everythin' smells and tastes uv goat.' 'Ah,' I said to 'n, sez I, 'they'm a bit of a noseful if thee bissn't use' to't.'

"And then he went on to tell me that there was another reason for wantin' to get shot of young Billy. It was his wife, he said, Mrs Carter. She'd got it into her 'ead there was a devil in that goat. She reckoned there was a funny look about'n. Somebody went an' told her the Old Nick hisself went about in the semblance of a goat. 'Twas playing on her mind, like. She said that if the goat didn't go, she would...

"Got another fag on ther?" Farmer asked at this point. He always managed to punctuate his stories with requests for a fag. They always came when you wanted to hear more.

"Thanks," he said. "You'm a gennelman."

He lit it and went on. "'Give us two quid,' I said, 'and I'll take'n off thee hands.' I had it in mind to sell'n on to Jobey Lukins—he do want somethink to kip down the weeds round his allotments. I'll kip'n in me greenhouse, jus' for the night, I thought. Ther ain't nuthin' in there he can get his teeth into.

Even goats can't eat glass. But there, I've always said, you can't never get to the bottom of 'em; goats is a race apart, my son.

"When I come down to get thik billy-goat the nex' day thee's never sin anythin' like it. 'Twas as if a gert starm had struck my greenhouse. There was glass everywhere. Piles on it. All in bits. Thik goat had pushed droo the main support and brought 'n down."

"What happened to the goat?" I asked.

"Oh, he! He were all right. Goats is like cats; they got nine loives. Nex' I heard was complaints from they over the Patch that the gypsies had raided their gardings. But I knew 'tweren't no gypsies—it were thik goat—and then, bust me, if 'er didn' get the homing instinc'. 'E were on his way back-yer when a gert car went into'n on the road outside and this-yer feller in a black suit come rushin' up, asking who'a belonged to.

"At first I thought I'd say I didn't know for a'd put a gert dent in the front o' this car but I could see the feller were anxious about the hanimal...

"'I'm afraid I've killed it,' he said.

"'I'm afraid you 'ave, mister,' says I. 'Pity, 'Tis a very valuable goat, that.'

"'It shouldn't have been on the road,' he says.

"'No, a'shouldn't,' I agreed, 'but you come round that carnder at a pretty tidy lick, mind.'

"He looked at thik goat, stretched out on the ground and he looked at the dent in his car and he says to me 'Tell you what I'll do,' he says. 'You just get rid of the hevidence,' he says, 'and here's a tenner for your trouble.'"

"You did pretty well out of that, Farmer."

"Ahhh," he said contentedly, "not so bad. 'Specially as the old goat weren't dead, arter all. Bruised and stiff, mind, but 'twas kinchusion what laid'n low. I sold'n to Jobey Lukins

after, to keep the weeds down. Tell 'ee what, squire, I got a lovely little kid at this moment, just right fer your lawn."

"No thanks," I said.

"They'm a wonder for keeping away the door-to-doors," he said.

"I'm like Mrs Carter," I said. "I can't stand the smell."

That was the only time I ever heard Farmer openly swank about an achievement "Now I'm lucky, I be." he said smugly. "I got no sense of smell at all. Not a whiffin! I was born wi'out it."

Lamplight

MY WORLD, WHEN I WAS YOUNG, WAS A WORLD OF COTTAGES half-hidden in leafy lanes. Dappled with sunlight in summer or dripping with rain in winter. Shadowy and dark at night, for lighting was a luxury of town. Our lanes were lit by moonlight or not at all.

Indoors, there was the magic of lamplight—a pool of yellow light round the oil lamp—and, beyond that, darkness. It seemed all that much darker because of the circle of yellow light. Corners of rooms were mysterious, staircases ominous, the world outside the lamplit circle full of hidden dangers.

All the wonder of lamplight vanished when the gas and electric came. They showed up every corner of a room, every detail. There were no mysterious corners, no unguessed-at horrors—everything was revealed as starkly ordinary.

I don't think you can really appreciate the tales of old storytellers unless you read or hear them by lamplight. They were not intended for the bright and breezy world of electric light.

Ghost stories really meant something then and I can still recall the horror of the unknown when Silas told one of his tales, sitting just beyond the light of the lamp on the table, taking an occasional pinch of snuff.

Our lane

He wasn't a relation. He lived on his own in a cottage down by Billy Baber's Hill. Retired from work by age and rheumatics, he made a few pence with his herbal remedies and cadged a few drinks with his stories. His one luxury was snuff and he inhaled it, delicately, from the back of his hand.

"See you've got a new lamp, Mrs Wilshire," he said. "Real beauty. Gives a lovely light."

She told him proudly that it was an Aladdin and he said that reminded him of the fairy story. You know, Aladdin's lamp. Well, of course, I knew all about Aladdin and his wonderful lamp because I'd seen the pantomime at the old Gaff, as they used to call the Theatre Royal in those days.

Gran said it was a good story but a bit silly. Whoever heard of a magic lamp!

Silas drew a deep breath. It meant there was a story here. Inspiration was on him.

"I use' to have a magic lamp," he said. "No, don't laugh. I mean it, missis. A magic lamp. Not like Aladdin's. You couldn' rub'n and have the jeany come up and ask 'ee in a thunderous gert voice what was your will. Mine wasn't so helpful. He had a habit of goin' out. Just when you needed'n."

"You'd be sat there in the room of a night, wi' every window shut and not a breath of air and it'd start. A rooshin' of the wind down the chimley, all the room in an uproar and, in the midst of it all—the lamp'd go out.

"Funny thing was, you'd be sat there, quaking in the dark, and the wind would die away. There'd be a deep silence. You never knew such a silence. Talk about hear a pin drop! You could hear the crickets under the stones o' the hearth and your own heart beating. You'd wait, expectin' something to happen and there'd be a little squeakin' sound, like a bat in the chimley. Not words, just a bit of a whisper. You'd strain your ears to it but 'twas just out of earshot. And then you'd light up the lamp again and tell yourself 'twas fancy."

Gran would laugh comfortably.

"You got a wonderful imagination, Silas," she said. "Where is it to, now then—this lamp of yours?"

"Had to get rid of 'n, missis. Couldn' stand the strain. 'Twasn't too bad when it happened once a fortnit. But 'twas getting to be every night! I told meself 'twas the weather but I knew it weren't. Even when 'twas a still night the wind'd whistle in the chimley and then t'would come into the room, whirl about 'ee, dout the light, and whisper.

"But you couldn't distinguish any words?"

"No, thank the Lard! I didn't want to! When it began 'twas just a whisper, out of earshot but at last it got to be louder— as if the spirit, or whatever 'twas, got stronger and was tryin' to tell me summat. A sort of gibbering noise. Hard to explain. You could *nearly* make out what 'twas, but not quite. I did listen, with a quaking heart, but to no avail."

"Pity," Gran said. "I should 'a liked to know what 'twas. Might 'a bin a message from beyond."

"Ah," he said, taking a pinch of snuff. "Thass why I got rid of 'un."

"What, the lamp?" I said listening in the chimney corner.

"It was gettin' to be too much of a good thing, my son. Every night 'twas gettin' that much clearer. I was on the verge of hearing what 'twas he was trying to tell I and, fact was, I didn't care to know. So I sold 'n to Potto..."

"Poor old Potto!" Gran said. "Did you explain about the wind and that?"

"No, I thought it might put 'n off the purchase."

"It would," Gran said. "He was a very imaginative man. I often wondered what happened that night..."

"Ah," said Silas. "We shall never know, missis. 'Twas a mystery, that was. The police came up and examined the place, you know. After they'd took his body to the crowner. But they was mystified. Not a mark on 'em. Nothing touched and nothing stolen. Potto was just sat there, in a chair, starin' in front of 'n, s'if he'd seen a ghost. Heart attack, s'know. Only to be expected really. His father went the same way."

"Let's see, it was evening, wasn't it?" Gran said.

"So they reckon. About ten or 'leben. Funny, really..."

"Why?" I asked "Why funny?"

"The lamp wasn't lit. Full of paraffin, plenty of wick—but seem as though something must 'a blown the lamp out—the glass was smoky." He laughed "They ast me if I wanted 'n back—the lamp, I mean—but I said No thanks. He's a good lamp, I said, let'n go to somebody in the family. A cousin of his'n, up North, come down and took'n. Said he needed a good lamp for his workshop. Just the job, really."

"How was that then, Silas?" Gran asked, stitching away in the lamplight at a green silk dress.

Silas too a pinch of snuff from the back of his hand.

"He was in a fair way of business up in Yorkshire, missis. Not an undertaker, see, but he made coffins. Need a good lamp, in that trade. In his workshop."

"Did you," I asked, "hear what happened to him?"

"Well," he began, "it's funny you should ask..."

Gran knew from my voice I was tense as a spring. I was very imaginative as a boy.

"Silas, that's enough for one night !" she said sharply. "You'll be giving the boy nightmares."

Silas said slyly, "It's all right, missis. I shan't give'n any nightmares. I was only going to say that I heard he was delighted with the old lamp. Best he'd ever had. Looked a treat that old lamp did. 'Twas solid brass, a lovely ornament—in among the coffins. No trouble at all. He said, in a letter, that it almost looked—at home, if you know what I mean."

Father Christmas

O NE OF MY OLD MAN'S FAVOURITE EXPRESSIONS was "quids-in". If you were "quids-in", you were doing all right! Another was "sup-me-bob"—this was an expletive, an expression of surprise. Must have been a contraction of "So help me, God!" but Father didn't know that: he used it, because, on the docks, everyone used it.

He was peculiar, in some ways. He didn't like Christmas. I don't suppose it is much fun, if you're short of money, and it's a bad time of year down at the docks, with not many ships coming in. If you didn't work, you weren't paid, in those days.

Anyway, he always ridiculed the old gentleman in the red cloak, and the giving and receiving of presents which cost you dear and weren't what you wanted.

"Terrible waste o' money," he grumbled. They've only got to hear a few carols and see some holly and mistletoe, and they goes mad."

We solved the problem of Christmas presents eventually, by an "arrangement". He gave me something *he* wanted, and I gave him something *I* wanted. Then on Christmas morning we solemnly returned our presents. It worked out quite well!

I remember one year I gave him a map of the Mendips, and he gave me a magnifying glass. That must have been later in life, when he couldn't see to read the Obituaries in the evening paper.

But that was after I was grown up. When I was a kid, Mother bought the presents. She loved Christmas. All the shops lit up, the decorations, Christmas trees, holly—Mother would get all excited, and boil the Christmas puddings in basins, ten or twelve of them; enough, Father said, to bung up our insides for the rest of the year.

As I say, Mother bought the presents. One year, I remember,

she bought me a mouth-organ. It drove the old man mad. He told her she should have more sense.

"Givin' a thing like that to a boy who can't play'n," he said: "it's like givin' a hand-grenade to a hottentot. Me head's fair splitting!"

"It's Christmas, Gilbert!"

"Christmas!" he said disgustedly. "'Tis more like bleedin' bedlam!"

"The boy's got to practise."

"Practise? If he'd a practise ten years, he on't master that thing. All he da do is blow, suck, suck, blow—it may be practice to somebody tone-deaf, but I got an ear for music, and I tell 'ee straight, it's drivin' me up the wall."

In the end, he couldn't stand it any longer, and he gave me sixpence to go and play outside.

"Go and annoy the neighbours," he said, "I can't stick it no longer. It's like twenty cats being sick. Sup-me-bob, I wonder sometimes whether your mother wants to be rid of me. She knows I've got sensitive ears."

So I went round to the neighbours, with my mouth-organ, playing carols, and it was quite surprising how generous they were. Perhaps they had sensitive ears too!

Shortly after Christmas, however, the mouth-organ vanished, and though I searched high and low, it was not to be found. I reckon it's probably lying in the mud at the bottom of Avonmouth dock.

My sister Stella had a pram that year. She had no dolly to put in it. Mum and Dad couldn't run to both, so she made do with a stocking, filled with paper. Father drew a face in indelible pencil on the top and tied it into shape with string. The arms and legs weren't too good, and the final result was what you might call grotesque.

She said she couldn't cuddle it.

"Pretend," Mother said, but there was a limit to pretending.

Anyway, she only had to wait twelve months, till the next Christmas, for a real doll. I remember it. China, it was, with a simpering face and eyes that opened and closed. If you pressed the squeaker in the small of its back, it was supposed to say Mama. Only they must have pronounced it differently in Japan, or else it didn't work properly. What came out was a sort of broken squawk. This was another thing that got on Father's nerves. He said it was more like the death agonies of a rooster than a baby saying Mama.

However, she dressed it up, put it in the pram, and took it out to show off to her friends in the street. Almost immediately, there was an agonised cry and a crash.

She had tipped up the new pram, negotiating the kerb, and her new doll was lying in the gutter. We rushed out to see what had happened, and at the awful sight Father let loose a few ripe expressions that were usually reserved for careless crane drivers.

The doll, the china doll, that had cost one-and-eleven-pence in Bristol, was in a hundred fragments. The eyes had fallen out and rolled away. The squeaker that said Mama was waterlogged in a puddle. We picked up the pieces, but Stella refused to touch them. She wanted her dolly, she sobbed, and Mother said,

Gran, Mother, Stella and I (clockwise)

"And so you shall, dear. Your Father's a dab hand with the egg-white. Don't you worry. He'll soon have it fixed. You won't know the difference."

"Whassmean?" Father demanded. "Look facts in the face,

Alice. That doll's had it!"

My sister burst into tears. Mother told him not to be unreasonable. After all, it was Christmas. She'd waited all the year for that doll, and then – a slip – and there it was, broken.

"You ought to have known, when you bought'n," Father said, wearily. "Cassn't get 'em made of rubber? You know she's rough with things."

He grumbled, but in the end he got to work with the egg-white, and worked on that doll all day. It ruined our Christmas dinner, seeing him there, wild-eyed and unshaven, with a strong smell of egg-white around him.

Eventually, quite late in the evening, it was finished. "What's think of that, then?" he asked, proudly handing the china doll to my sister.

She took one look at it and burst into tears.

"What's the matter with 'er, now?" he demanded.

"They eyes don't look quite right," Mother hazarded. "She looks sort of… squint-eyed."

"Well, I can't help. P'raps the wire got a bit bent. It's all very well for they Japs, they got small hands, but it's a hell of a job to get 'em right. As 'tis, they on't shut. I had to glue 'em in, see."

"Pity," Mother said. "Try the Mama-thing, dear."

She did, and a sort of strangled
gasp came from the doll.

"It works," Father said, but once again my sister had started to cry.

"What is it now?" he asked.

"She looks... she looks old," my sister said, "all those cracks."

"Well, o'course there's cracks, that's where I had to stick her together."

I could see what my sister meant by looking old. What with all the cracks, the doll didn't look like a baby. More like a squinting dwarf. Sinister at that!—When you come to think of it, it's surprising she turned out to be such a good mother— my sister, I mean. She swapped the doll for some marbles. The boy opposite thought the doll looked a bit like his school-teacher, and he wanted it for "experiments". I had a suspicion that the "experiments" entailed sticking pins into the doll, hoping to evoke the powers of darkness. Anyway, it all turned out all right in the end. My sister turned out to be a dab hand at marbles. All for the best, when you come to think of it!

The author and his sister Stella

Jonah's Return

N O DOUBT FOR SOME PERSONAL AND INTIMATE REASON his parents had christened him Jonah. But he never told anyone, of course. To the world he was John, locally Jack and, to those few he got drunk with, Jacko.

They were a funny family, even for us. Old man Arscott was known to be peculiar in his habits long before he defiled the side wall of Hebron and was excommunicated.

It was said that his wife, Maggie, had told one of her relations that he had dirty habits. Pressed to explain, she had whispered that he never used the privy. Mind you, that was not surprising. Their privy was far from inviting. All the cottages in our hamlet had outside toilets, mostly with cesspits nearby, and often at the end of the garden. Some were noisome, most draughty, all uncomfortable. In the dark they were difficult to find, unless your nose and feet knew the way, and that was why every cottage had a commode. We called them night stools.

Old man Arscott, it seems, never used his privy because it was dark, dirty and difficult to find. He had a commode with a cover on it which he ceremoniously placed in front of the open coal fire every morning so that he could relieve himself in comfort and warmth. His wife, being a Christian woman, had, from the first, tried to break him of the habit.

"It's one or the other of us," she said. "Either that thing goes or I do."

He told her to be reasonable. He couldn't be expected to catch his death of cold down the garden after all these years of comfort. She said it was worse than heathen. He thought the heathen probably had a lot of sense. Eventually she gave in, as she did over several other little matters. As I said, they were a funny family.

So when, in the course of time, they had a son, he was different from other boys. Admittedly he had the name to put up with but there was more to it than that. Right from the start he was a loner.

And, when he grew up, he would never use a particular pub as his local. Now this was a sort of heresy to us: like going to a different church or chapel every Sunday. Sometimes he'd have a pint at the Crown, then move on to the Star, then up the King Billy and, finally, round the Shant. There was no system or pattern to his drinking. Or his life. He would take a job then leave it for no reason; stay home for a week or two then vanish without trace. He might be away for a couple of days or a month, then he'd return as though he'd only been down the shop for some fags and start work with passionate fervour on a hen-coop or a pigeon-loft as though his life depended on it.

Old Arscott would threaten and bully him, his mother would weep, but Jacko went his own way...

He became big and broad-shouldered as he grew up; a giant of a man, over six feet and big-boned. And then he walked out one day and disappeared. When he came back, six months later, he was a soldier.

There must have been a row because neighbours said there were shouts and screams and furniture broken and, next day, Mrs Arscott emerged red-eyed, whilst Old Arscott had a black eye, a split lip and a limp. Jacko had finally taken exception to the commode in the kitchen, smashed it to bits with an axe and laid down a new set of rules. Their house was in an uproar. He had ransacked it to find his father's gold.

Of course everyone knew that somewhere, is some nook or cranny or behind a wall, Old Arscott kept his hoard. He was a miser. His family had all been misers. Somewhere, hidden away, there was wealth untold. To be fair, Jacko didn't want all of it. He was only asking for his share. Like the Prodigal Son. But Old Arscott was not a practising Christian. He didn't approve of prodigal sons and, in spite of eye, lip and limp, Jacko did not receive his portion.

He must be home on leave, we conjectured, watching him stride from one pub to another. But a week went by and he didn't rejoin his troop. What was even more sinister was that his uniform, smart and clean when he first arrived, became grubby and was then abandoned. Except for the boots, of course. They were very good boots !

Old Mr and Mrs Arscott were frightened of him. They had made him, between them, but they couldn't control him. He tyrannised their home and, as if that wasn't bad enough, he was rude to the regulars at the locals. Landlords hated the sight of him. But they couldn't say so. He was, as I say, very strong. And he always paid for his drinks, never caused a physical disturbance and—fortunately for the publicans— seldom stayed long.

Wherever he went he was unwelcome, knew it and seemed to revel in it. The crisis came when he followed in his father's footsteps to the extent of defiling the Hebron wall. Old Man Arscott had been guilty of this crime once, many years before, and it had caused a stir then. But that was in the dark and without thinking. Jacko's sin was premeditated.

"With all the other walls in the place to choose from," Clarice Bollom said, scandalised, "he had to use *that* wall. Where he'd attended Sunday School as a boy and knew how touchy the Superintendent is about dogs, let alone human beings with souls to be lost."

A version was retailed to the Superintendent himself and the matter was raised with the Almighty on the following Sunday. It was humiliating for his mother. She had been a member of the Women's Bright Hour for twenty years and had a certificate for Bible study. Of course, no names were mentioned in their prayers but everybody knew they were praying for a judgment on Jacko. And they waited, in fear and trembling, for a thunderbolt to strike him or maybe (one can't expect miracles) for him to trip over a log and break his leg.

Strangely Jacko survived and started to make a ritual of it. He had to pass the side wall on his way home from the pubs and, as often as not, he would water the wall despite all that vestry meetings and patrols could do.

When we were on the point of doubting the efficacy of prayer or the sanctity of the Tabernacle, our prayers were answered. A policeman and three soldiers, one with stripes, came to Arscotts' cottage. There were sounds of a struggle. Then the army removed Jacko who, it seems, had deserted. We breathed a sigh of relief.

Down at Hebron they were smug. They could afford to be. Their prayers had been answered. The desecrator had received his just punishment, which, as they said, only went to prove...

It was a mistake to have called him Jonah, perhaps. Because he came back. The Leviathan cast him forth; he returned home. Constable Pugh was alerted, the neighbours waited apprehensively for fireworks but, strangely, nothing happened. Jacko seemed to be a changed man. His mother and father treated him warily but reported that he was strangely silent. All he did, they said, was *read books*. This strange practice was alien to that family. Jacko had never been a reader in the past. Now he appeared to be lost to the world.

When he emerged, at last, from his seclusion, he was clean

and well-behaved, did not visit the pubs or chapel and soon obtained regular work on the buildings.

On Sundays he would disappear all day, complete with a pile of books. It was all very strange and the answer, when it came, was quietly shocking.

There was a tap on the door and, as she always did, Gran called out "Come on in." The door was never closed when she was working.

Into our front parlour stepped a man with a clutch of books wearing a dark suit, collar and tie, polished boots and a hat which he removed politely as he stepped inside.

It was Jacko.

"I'm working for the Cause," he said.

Gran must have looked puzzled because he added, by way of explanation, in a hushed voice that conveyed worlds of meaning, "I've seen the light."

"Ah, that's good, Jack. Yes. Glad to hear it."

"It's all here," he said earnestly, tapping a paper-covered magazine. "I was lost, Mrs Wilshire, like a lamb. I wandered from the fold. But I've been found."

"Yes," said Gran, looking at his suit and polished shoes. "I can see you have."

"For threepence," he said, "you can share the message. You can learn the way to Peace."

As my gran was about the most peaceful person I've ever encountered I failed to see why she needed anybody else to tell her, but I suppose it was worth the money to find out what had changed the man. Threepence was a lot in those days but she found three pennies and handed them over. In exchange she received a cheap-looking pulp magazine which Jacko assured her would change her life.

After he'd gone I wanted to know what the magazine was about.

Gran put on her spectacles and studied it, perplexedly, for

some time.

"Well?" I asked.

"That Jonah," she said, musingly, "he's gone and got religion. He's a Jehovah's Witness."

When she told Granfer at tea-time she said, "There you are, Fred, as I've always said, God works in a mysterious way, His wonders to perform."

But Granfer, as usual, was unimpressed.

"Sarah," he said, "I've told you before and I'll tell 'ee again you do put too much salt in these potatoes."

The Old Nick and Alfie

THIS ALFIE WAS A SIMPLE SOUL, strong in the arm but weak in the noddle, who lived with his widowed mother not far from the Green Dragon. He was known as Two-Pint or Alfie Two-Pint.

His mother was a Good Woman, a bit on the religious side, a few too many principles but clean as a new pin.

The trouble was that Alfie liked his drop of beer. His mother said it would be scandalous if he drank in our village among her neighbours so, when he wanted a drink, he had to walk a mile or more along country lanes to Mangotsfield. Even so, his mother warned him that he was taking a risk. Beer, she said, was the Devil's Brew and, one of these nights, if he didn't watch out or had one over the odds, the Old Nick'd have him.

Alfie didn't take much account of Old Nick. He liked the conviviality of a pub, he enjoyed a good long drink but he had it worked out that *three* pints was safe. Four might put his soul in jeopardy. So he stuck to three and walked back to Downend whistling or humming to himself without any feeling of guilt at all.

All would have gone well but, one evening, at the Red Lion, he forgot himself. So much so that, in the excitement of playing dominoes, he drank four pints; four, instead of his usual three.

I said he was a simple soul and, although he pretended not to take a lot of account of his mother's moralising, he felt guilty...

It was a very dark, still night. One of those nights when clouds drift across the face of a full moon and you're in darkness one minute, the next the moon emerges like a huge great eye looking down at you.

Alfie knew, the moment he heard it, that he'd gone too far. The Old Nick was after him! He quickened his pace but, as he did so, the pace of his pursuer quickened too. His mother had told him that the devil wore chains. Now he could hear them coming after him—CHINK, CHINK, CHINK! You'd never suppose one pint could do it! he thought to himself. But his mother had warned him not to go over the mark. Now he regretted his momentary weakness. CHINK, CHINK, CHINK! went the chains. Alfie broke into a trot.

As soon as he trotted the sound of chains quickened. Sweat broke out on his brow. The moon plunged behind a cloud and Alfie could almost feel the hot breath of the Fiery Fiend on his neck.

He tried to remember a prayer; hummed a hymn or two; but it was no use. The Old Nick was after him, CHINK, CHINK, CHINK, and he broke into a run.

Of course we know it's no use running in a situation like that. But Alfie thought, if only I can get home, Mother'll drive him off. Her Goodness will save me. He won't get me if she can stop him. So he yelled out "Mother, Mother, open up quick, the Old Nick's after me!"

She must have heard his shouts because she had the cottage door open as he tore up the garden path...

"Quick, Mother—bolt the door!" he gasped. "He nearly got me."

She looked at him accusingly.

"You've had one too many!" she said.

"I have," he admitted, "and I won't ever touch more than the two ever again. But you'd better get out the Good Book, in case. I can hear him out there—listen!"

They listened and, sure enough, there was a CHINK, CHINK of chains outside and a scratching at the door.

"You've had a narrow escape, my son," his mother said.

Alfie admitted it and decided to give the Red Lion a miss—at any rate for a week or two. His mother said the safest thing would be to sign the pledge but Alfie wouldn't go that far. He thought that if he left it alone for a week and then cut it down to two he'd be all right.

His mother didn't press him too much. She knew that his visits to Mangotsfield provided him with a bit of life so she warned him to leave early and carry a Holy Bible in his pocket, which he did.

She didn't tell him that, when she'd opened the door on the morning after Old Nick had chased him, she'd found a dog on the mat outside. Peter, his name was. Alfie always made a fuss of him when he saw him in the cottage by the Red Lion where he lived. Hanging from Peter's collar was a length of chain with which he'd been attached to his kennel and which he'd broken off to follow his friend, Alfie.

He must have felt lonely chained up to that kennel and when he'd seen his old friend, Alfie Two-Pint, well, he'd broken loose.

Alfie's mother quietly took him back and his owners were no doubt pleased to see him. She didn't tell Alfie, of course, it would have spoilt everything. And, after all, she thought, it could well have been a Sign.

"I shouldn't tell anybody about the other night," she said casually. "They'd think you was drunk, that 'twas imagination."

He didn't, but it was noticeable that he left the Red Lion before closing time and never drank more than two pints from that time on. On nights when the moon was full, he didn't venture out at all.

"You'd better stay in tonight," his mother would say. "'Tis a full moon and he'll be looking for sinners." And, just to make sure, she'd retrieve the Good Book from his pocket. "You won't need this tonight, my son," she'd say.

The Day War Broke Out

T HE DAY WAR BROKE OUT…" he used to begin… "my missis said to me 'You 'ave to stop it.'"

This was the opening of one of the late Robb Wilton's monologues. If you're under fifty you've probably never heard of him but in the old days—before they ruined broadcasting with pictures—he was one of the characters of the BBC. *Mr Muddlecombe, JP*—that was one of his series. And he was one of the Great Ones of Music Hall.

My old man thought a lot of Robb Wilton. Not that he was anything like him, but Dad collected characters and Robb Wilton—like Billy Bennett, Stainless Stephen and Harry Tate—was a character all right.

Talking of the day war broke out—that was the very day that two chaps called Sid and Jack installed our Anderson shelter. They started by digging a hole and they were hard at it when Mr Chamberlain's announcement came over the radio…

"I have to tell you that, since eleven o'clock this morning, this country and Germany are at war."

My old man nearly swallowed his fag in the emotion of the moment. Not that we were surprised, you know, but he was a very emotional man really.

"Here, Lewis, go down the garden and tell Sid and Jack," he said. To my mother he added, "Better tell 'em. It'll make 'em realise."

"Realise what?"

"That they're on war work," Father said. "They was tellin' me, earlier on, that some of the neighbours been makin' fun of 'em. You know, askin' if it'll make a good buffalo trap. Saying as if they happens to come across coal to let 'em have a couple of hundredweight to be going on with."

"Some people!" Mother said disgustedly. "They don't deserve to have shelters, some people don't."

"They'll be the first to shout when the bombs start falling," Father said.

Anyway I went down between the rows of runner beans to tell Sid and Jack there was a war on. And they emerged from the hole they were digging for a quick fag.

"Mind, I knew it was comin'," Jack said. "That 'Itler bin askin' for it this long time."

"Aaarh," commented Sid with a struggle—he hadn't yet mastered his false teeth and had some difficulty getting them going. "I dunno about 'Itler being in for it. Reckon we be."

"He won't never get *yer*," Jack said. "His nerve'll crack."

Sid sorted out his teeth and looked gloomy.

"Aarrh, I dunno. The way I looks at it—if he don't never get 'ere we'm wasting our time digging these 'oles. If he *do* get here, these perishing 'oles ain't going to be much good."

It was at that point my old man arrived on the scene.

"'Ave one of mine!" he said generously to mark the auspicious occasion, "before he sends they bombers over."

All three laughed.

They gazed up at the sky. It was clear. Blue. Empty.

"When d'ee reckon you'll be done then?" said Dad indicating the shelter-to-be with a Woodbine.

"Oh, we shall finish tomorrow."

Father nodded "How about you chaps," he says. "Have you got shelters?"

Sid said they didn't need one; they had a cellar. And Jack said they didn't need one because Hitler wouldn't last six months. My old man said it would make a good place to store fruit and vegetables but he hoped he'd never have to risk his neck getting into it. They all three laughed again.

Rather significantly, no fewer than three little kids came in during the day to ask when Sid and Jack would be down their part of the road. They were still waiting for their Anderson and their mothers said better get a move on or it'll be too late.

"Ain't that typical?" Jack exclaimed. "They bin making fun of us up till now. I can't count the number of blokes who've told us to push off. That bald-headed feller in number sixty-three, he was quite rude—wasn't 'er, Sid?—'You can take yer shovels and go,' he said. 'You ain't touching *my* onions and I don't want you clumping round my garden neither.' Now I s'pose they'll be quarrellin' whose turn 'tis next."

"Oh, ah," remarked Father. "You'll be in great demand now, you chaps. Everybody'll be thinking about bombs, you mark my words."

"They 'ont never get 'ere!" Jack repeated, but already his voice lacked conviction. "I give'n six months," he said.

Sid shook his head. "Don't talk like that!" he said. "You'll talk us out of a job."

At that moment Mother came out and asked them if they felt like a cup of tea. Naturally they said Yes and adjourned to our kitchen leaving my old man and me beside the hole in the ground.

"Who can tell," he said profoundly, "what the future holds?"

I agreed whilst making a mental reservation about the future of the garden for cabbages. My old man said it reminded him of the trenches in the First World War. "Just fancy," he said, "this might be No Man's Land!" He looked at the hole through a cloud of cigarette smoke. "Who can tell?" he asked it. "Who can tell?"

They finished the Anderson on the day after. For a year it wasn't used, apart from storing potatoes in and then—in 1940—came the first big raid on Bristol. After that we got to know the shelter like the back of our hands. Well, actually, Mother, my sister and I probably knew it better. Not my old man. When searchlights were sweeping the sky and Big

Bertha was pounding away on Purdown, Father stayed in bed. He said we could do as we pleased but he wasn't going to be buried in a hole in the garden, not he. He'd go in comfort if he had to go at all. Mother said he was selfish but he could be very stubborn, my old man.

Anyway, we survived the war. My granfer lost a pear tree to a German bomb, but that's another story—we emerged unscathed, as you might say, which made us luckier than some.

And then, after the war was over, a couple of workmen came round to take away the Anderson. Not Sid and Jack. I don't know what happened to them, no, this was two different blokes...

"Here, don't fill it in," said my old man, "jus' take the top part, leave the bottom where 'tis."

I didn't catch his drift at first. He explained "I've just had an ideal. All me life I bin wanting a lake, like the gentry get. That hole from the shelter'll make a lovely pond."

It did, too. Father knew a bloke on the docks who specialised in ponds... you know, two kinds of pondweed, water snails, water lilies, reeds, carp, everything.

We all caught his enthusiasm. I planted a willow tree by the side of it, we were given a frog by the boy in twenty-nine, newts appeared from nowhere—and, in a couple of years, that pond was part of our life. Father made a very nice garden seat out of two wooden bunks and we put some crazy paving round it—I tell you, that pond was a picture!

On fine summer evenings it was our hearth, outdoors. We used to sit there and reminisce and get bitten to pieces by the gnats—who'd somehow got it into their heads that the pond had been put there for their benefit!

"Remember the day it was put 'ere?" Father would say. "Sid and Jack? Seems like yesterday."

"September the third it was," Mother pointed out.

"Little did we know then," Father lugubriously puffed smoke up at the gnats, "that we would shelter in it when the bombs came down."

"You never did," Mother said. "You stayed in bed."

"Little did we know," Father went on, "that one day we'd convert the old Anderson to a fish pond and that we would have our own frog."

There was a pause while we all luxuriated in the possession of a fish pond.

Then my sister said "Little did we know that one day we would see, in among the reeds..."

"What?" Father said sharply.

"The corpse of poor old Tiddles," she said.

"*What?*" we all cried.

"Over there—look," she pointed.

She was right. It was Tiddles and he was certainly very dead. His four paws were pointing skyward.

"D'you reckon," Mother asked, "he fell in?"

"Must 'ave unless he committed suicide," Father said. "He never seemed to be what you might call a *happy* cat."

"We'd better tell 'em," I said. "They've been looking for him."

Father whistled through his remaining teeth.

"Better not," he advised. "We don't wanna be blamed, They'd say it was our fault, keeping an open pond, for anythin' to fall in."

"Well we can't leave him there, Gilbert. You'll have to bury him."

So Father fished out Tiddles with the garden fork and we planted him. Not silently, at dead of night, like Sir John Moore at Corunna, but when the next-doors were at the pictures.

You may ask what all this has to do with the day war broke out and the answer is nothing, nothing at all.

Except that you might say Tiddles was our one and only war casualty.

Only it was peace time then.

As Father philosophised, "You never know what lies ahead. What's round the next corner..."

And, as usual, my old man was right.

Here I am, all dressed-up, on the verge of manhood

Fallen Hero

WHEN I WAS YOUNG THE WORLD WAS A VERY DIFFERENT PLACE. Life was hard but there was a sort in innocence that's been lost. We had ideals then that would be laughable now. And there were boys and girls— ordinary, ragged, not very well-washed kids—who inspired us. Somehow they had the mark of greatness on them.

...Like Stephen.

Trying to recapture those days is terribly difficult because it isn't just that *we* were young; the world seemed young, too. There was a spring freshness about life. We had our heroes and we worshipped them. We read Stevenson, Henty and Rudyard Kipling if we were boys and—well—I don't know what the girls read, but we spent our money on the weeklies— *Magnet* and *Gem*, *Wizard* and *Skipper*, *Adventure* and *Hotspur*.

Stephen was exactly like the heroes of these tales. He was thin with fair hair which waved slightly; modest and intelligent, fair to a fault and good at sport. It was typical of those days that, when he won, he apologised and when he lost he praised the other chap. He was the perfect hero, in fact, but for *one* little flaw, *one* little weakness...

Girls.

The rest of us didn't bother much about girls. Well, one didn't, in those days until one was well into one's teens and then only as a sort of game. But then Stephen was a year older than the rest of us and, of course, he hadn't a sister. If you had a sister you hadn't any illusions about them. Stephen hadn't a sister and that's why he was so susceptible...

I can see him now, organising a new game—he was good at that—inventing as he went along, pretending because we hadn't anything except imagination to play with.

"You three," he'd say, "will be the Indians. We two are the

Settlers. We're in camp. We've jus' settled down for the night when you Indians creep up on us, take us by su'prise. You make us captives. Then you torture us so's we'll tell. You torture us—not for real, o' course, then you tie us to a tree and dance round us.

His young brother would object. Clifford always objected. Unlike Stephen he was made that way. Objectionable. He would never be a hero. He picked his nose.

"'Tain't fair!" Clifford said. "I don't wanta be a Nindian."

Stephen would be astonished.

"I thought you'd want to be an Indian, Cliff," he'd say. "You'll get all the fun—creeping through the grass, tying us up, torturing us."

It was true that Clifford enjoyed the torture bit. He liked cutting worms in half and pulling butterflies' wings off. Not a bit like Stephen.

"I know you," he said darkly. "You'll escape somehow, you always do, and make us three look silly."

Well, of course, there was some truth in that. Stephen did always escape. Talked his way out of trouble. Made Alfie, Clifford and me look silly. When we complained he said, "All right, then, we'll play the game your way. This time Cliff and Shirty can be the Settlers."

No, that wasn't any good either. Clifford, who was short and fat and cheated if he got the chance, said he didn't care what game we played as long as he was on Stephen's side. Somehow it was always that side that got the fun!

But that was the point. Stephen's side got all the fun because Stephen was in it. And, equally, Cliff's side always got the worst of it because *he was in it*. Even if he had to die in the course of a game (imaginary, of course) Stephen would die heroically leaving the rest of us mere survivors.

When we played "Greyfriars" he *had* to be Harry Wharton, captain of the Remove and leader of the Famous Five. He

wouldn't ask for the part. Didn't need to. He *was* Harry Wharton, except, as I say, in the matter of girls...

I told you he hadn't a sister. That meant he didn't know what they were really like. He had no idea that they told tales, struck attitudes, enjoyed seeing boys pushed around and, above all, used their femininity as a weapon. Shirty and I had sisters and our sisters had friends so we *knew*, but poor old Stephen... well, it was tragic. Tragic!

He fell in love. Well, that goes without saying. The trouble was he chose all the wrong girls to fall in love with. We could have told him that but he wouldn't listen...

There was Sybil—she was blonde and pretty and empty-headed with a giggle for everything and a feeling for nothing. Eva was dark and unpredictable. Betty had enormous dark eyes and a look of innocence that would have been suspicious to anyone who had a sister. She was the worst of the lot because she told everything, with decorations, to her friends... afterwards.

To Stephen they were princesses in a fairy tale. He adored

them—not all at once, you know, but in succession. It was terrible to see him blush and go all tongue-tied in front of a girl who you knew wasn't worthy of tying up his tennis shoes.

Among us we decided that somebody had better tell him the facts of life before it was too late.

Clifford said he couldn't because he was his older brother and anyway he didn't know what girls were like himself. Alfie couldn't help much either because he never knew what to say.

"Somebody's got to tell him," Shirty said. "He's gone potty about that Betty Britton at the moment and she's leading him on. I heard her telling my sister, laughing about it. She told our Edna he's writing poetry to 'er now."

"Sup-me-bob!" said Alfie, who picked up these expressions from his father. "Poetry! He must be off his chump."

We drew lots for the task of telling Stephen and the result was the choice fell on me. I tried to get out of it but the others insisted.

"You promised you'd abide by it," they said. "Now you've got to keep your word."

So I tackled Stephen and told him and, after I'd been explaining to him that girls weren't all sugar and spice for about a quarter of an hour, I realised he wasn't even listening to me. He was far away. I must have mentioned the name of Betty and he went off into a sort of daydream telling me her eyes were like blue pools and all that sort of rubbish.

"You'll be sorry," I warned him. "You ought to stick to the things you know about. Books, History. Football. Cricket. *Sensible* things. Girls ain't worth bothering about. You don't read about girls in the *Wizard* or *Skipper*."

He dismissed boys' papers with a wave of the hand.

"I don't read that stuff any more," he said. "I'm reading Shakespeare."

I gaped at him. This was the end. How could *anybody* read Shakespeare—in their own time—because they *wanted* to?

He quoted bits of *Romeo and Juliet*. Obviously he saw himself as Romeo and Betty Britton as Juliet. It was ridiculous! She was thirteen.

"You'll lose your place in the school team," I warned, "if you moon about after girls."

You would have thought that would bring him to his senses.

All he said was: "*Cricket*! Who cares about cricket?"

After that I gave up. It seemed to me that anybody who could speak like that about cricket was past reasoning with.

"It's no good," I told the others, "he won't listen to reason. I think he's gone a bit queer in the head."

At first it seemed as though our life had lost its savour. Our world lay in fragments, our games were over, our revels, as Prospero says in *The Tempest*, are ended...

And then an extraordinary thing happened.

I fell for a girl called Kathy who had freckles and a turned-up nose. Shirty got in tow with a strange silent girl from Pucklechurch. Even Clifford babbled about some kid called June who played netball and lived at Staple Hill.

Before the summer was out we were as hopeless as Stephen—it must have been catching. The only exception was Alfie. He couldn't understand what all the fuss was about. Kept on boring us with talk of cricket and the Famous Five. We thought, privately, that poor old Alfie was a bit retarded or something.

Of course we didn't marry the girls. There were others. But we did, eventually, after the usual soul-searing crises, get married. Except Alfie. He's still wondering what it was all about and reading space stories.

Stephen? Oh, he's still around. You may know him. He teaches at a school these days. If I told you the name of the school you'd open your eyes a bit. But that would be telling!

I'll give you a clue, though... His name definitely isn't Stephen.

The Passing Show

MY OLD MAN HAD A FASCINATION FOR FAIRGROUNDS. If there was a carnival within two or three miles—down the Straits, Staple Hill park, Roddy Hill—he'd be there. His trilby and his fag were part of the scene!

This was so well known that one of his pals at work remarked, quite innocently: "Still get around the shows then, Gilb?"

"Whas's mean?" Father demanded.

"You know, the fairgrounds. Carnivals. I never been to one yet without seeing you there. I said to Bert Acker, t'other day, 'Gilb must have money in they roundabouts, I reckon; he watches 'em for hours.'"

The Whitsuntide Fair at Rodway Hill

"Thee's better mind what thee's sayin'!" Father warned. "I don't want to be thought of as a man who follows the shows around. S'matter o' fact I only goes for one reason."

"What's that, Gilb?"

"To see fools like you chucking your money around."

His favourite show was the Whitsuntide fair at Rodway Hill.

"I think I'll just go up as far as the Hill," he'd say. "See what's about."

"It'll be the same as it always is," Mother would say disparagingly. "Roundabouts. Side shows. Hoop-la. It's years since they had a fortune teller. Oh, well, if you're going, you might as well take the kids. Get 'em out of my way."

But Father didn't want to take two kids. He wanted to go on his own.

"Don't know what you see in showgrounds," Mother would grumble. "Should've thought you'd have grown out of 'em by this time. That's what they're for, children."

"Ah, you don't understand, Alice. It ain't the gambling and coconut shies. And it ain't the roundabouts. I likes to see behind the scenes."

That was true. You'd see him, fag-end stuck to his lip, in among the caravans, at the back of the Wall of Death or studying the workings of a steam engine whose bright paint and gleaming machinery never failed to mystify him.

Not *always*, though! He'd sometimes be seen among the crowd, just a trilby hat—he wasn't a big man—listening to the patter of the Chocolate King, hypnotised by the motion of the Gondolas, or one of the crowd around the side shows. If you taxed him with it he'd say that he disapproved of fairgrounds really.

"Terrible waste of money," he'd say. "You never see me chucking it about like that."

This was true enough. Father didn't chuck his money about because he didn't have any; though he said that if he had he wouldn't have wasted it in that way.

"What d'you go for then?" I'd ask.

"I s'pose it's the atmosphere," he said. "You sees a bit of life in there, behind the scenes."

"Yes, but you don't stay behind the scenes. I saw you, last time, listening to that bloke selling watches."

"Oh, well, I likes to be part of it sometimes. The Passing Show."

"I reckon there's more to it than you let on," Mother said. "What d'you always wear your best hat for? And why won't you take the children? I reckon," she said, watching him closely, "it's the girls."

The author with Stella at Staple Hill park

"What girls?"

"The young girls." She enumerated her suspicions. He was either eyeing the teenagers on the roundabouts or he was having thoughts about that buxom piece who ran the Hoop'la stall; or maybe he was hoping to meet up with one of his old flames.

"Your mother," he confided, "have got a suspicious mind. Women's all the same. They don't understand. No use to tell me it's the same as last time, that the noise and glitter is for kids. I know that. It's just that, now and then, I like to feel part of it. The Passing Show."

"I reckon you overdo this Passing Show business," I said critically. "Seems to me there's more in it than that."

"I'm surprised at you, Lewis," he said lyrically. "The whirling chair-o-planes all lit up against the night sky over Charnell; the over boats, the carved mirrors in the Gondolas; the hissing of steam and the shrieking of girls."

"There's more to it than that," I said doggedly.

"You'm talking like your mother," he said, "but I'll tell 'ee the truth. Only don't let on to your ma, mind, otherwise I'm done for… the fact is—now, not a word of this to anybody—I used to be sweet on a showman's daughter before I met your mother and she was gone on me."

"Nothing ever came of it then?"

He shrugged expressively.

"All that came between us," he said. "She loved the life and couldn't of left it. The mud and the sawdust, the steam and the noise was in her blood. I should have had to give up a settled life. 'Tis all moving about with them, here today and gone tomorrow... I still don't know how I should'a fitted in."

"Mother'd kill you, if she knew."

"I know," he said. "She've got a temper on her, your mother have. Funny thing, all the girls I ever cared about had tempers on 'em. I could never fathom whether 'twas because I liked girls with a bit of spirit or whether I brought out the worst in 'em."

"This girl," I asked, "the one you were sweet on, have you ever seen her since?"

"Oh, ah!" He looked sly. "Sees her every time I goes to the shows. Only she don't rec'nise me and I don't make meself known to her."

"Why not?"

"She got fat. Ugly with it. I stops in front of her sometimes but she don't know me from Adam. I pretends I'm interested in having a go at the coc'nuts. 'Come along, sir,' she sez. 'You're a strong man ain't you? Knock down a nut for your missis. Come on, be a sport sir.' I goes round the back of the vans and I thinks to meself, I might be in one o' they with a horde of kids or working me guts outs in among the machinery of the roundabouts." He paused and inhaled deeply—always a sign of profound thought. "Putting up tents and taking 'em down again," he said. "Never in one place for more'n a week."

"But you said you like to feel part of it," I reminded him. "You said it was romantic."

"Oh, well," he said, "in a way, it is. To they who go, not to they who works it. It ain't no bed of roses down the docks but

it's bloody Paradise alongside they showgrounds. I've watched 'em, in the back there, working away like beavers. And they caravans—I've seen inside 'em. They'm very nice, in their way, but thee cassn't compare 'em with a council house. There ain't room to swing a cat."

"Well, if you think it was a lucky escape," I said, "why d'you always go there? I should have thought you'd want to stay away."

"Ah, that's what thee's think!" he said happily. "When you'd'a get older, my son, you enjoys looking back and thinking what-might-have-bin. It's one of the pleasures of growing old."

His fag was down to the last gasp, in danger of burning his lip. He took it out and threw it away, always a tragic moment...

"Come to that," he said ,"and when thee's come down to it... it's the only pleasure thee's got left."

My Father—an observer in life

Patchwork

SHAKESPEARE WAS RIGHT, YOU KNOW. There comes a time and tide in the affairs of men which, taken at the flood, leads on to fortune. We all of us have these moments when we stand at a crossroads. Straight ahead for success. Fork right for sudden death. Left for good luck, second left for bad. For that one moment, it all depends…

And then we choose.

Speaking for myself, I've never really chosen the highways. Preferred the by-paths, myself. But there have been times, like when I was eight, when I dipped a toe in the tide, you might say…

Gran Wilshire was the village dressmaker, as I've told you. Worked from morning till night making dresses and blouses and skirts and underslips—stitching away in the light of our big front window or the glow of the paraffin lamp.

She didn't make a fortune at it because, although Gran worked hard, she loved spending money. And she was one of the few people I've ever known who loved giving it away.

Granfer was the opposite. He'd retired by the time I went to live there and his life was his pigs and his orchard. Whatever he made from his pigs and his apples he kept. Granfer never gave anything to anybody. Didn't see why he should!

They looked the part, too—she fat and silver-haired and happy, he morose and friendless, never short of a grouse and only happy when he heard some old enemy of his had died.

"I see by the paper old George Bissick is gone," he'd say. "He'll have some things to account for in the hereafter. Remember how he done me over that barley-meal? I never forgave'n for that."

"You don't want to speak ill of the dead," Gran said.

"I do. Living or dead, the man was a scoundrel."

I wasn't a participant, only a listener. I lived with them because there wasn't any room at home with Mum and Dad and, of course, I loved Gran and feared Granfer. She was kind and foolish; he was cautious and mean. I knew, with all the wisdom of an eight-year-old, that there was another side to the coin: that Gran was thriftless and Granfer thrifty, and sometimes it worried me that she gave so little thought for money.

For instance, she always undercharged folk who were poor and she gave away patchwork. That was the off-cuts of silk and satin, muslin and morocaine. Little girls used to call in and say "Can I have some patchwork, please, Mrs Wilshire? I want to make my dolly a dress."

"Yes, dear. There's a great pile of bits in that tea-chest over there. Help yourself."

Pondering this casual method of disposal I had an idea.

"Gran," I said "can I have the patchwork?"

"Yes, o' course; but what would you want with patchwork?"

"I'm gonna make it up into bundles and sell it."

"Sell patchwork? Poor dears, most on 'em couldn't afford it."

"Yes, they could. Most of 'em gets pocket money. I reckon they ought to pay for it."

She shook her head. "I couldn' never charge for patchwork."

"You don't need to. I will. I'll make it up into bundles and charge a ha'penny a time."

She agreed that wasn't extortionate and next time a little girl came to the door for patchwork, Gran referred her to me.

"Our Lewis is handling me patchwork. You'll have to speak to him."

"Ha'penny a bundle."

The little girl—actually she was older than me—refused to buy. She went off, crestfallen, and Gran wanted to call her back, tell her it was free. But I was adamant. "No ha'penny, no patchwork," I said. And to prove that my business instincts were right, the little girl came back the next day with a sulky look and a penny. She wanted *two* bundles.

"There you are, Gran," I said. "You've bin too soft with 'em. Now they've got me to deal with they won't get away with free patchwork no more."

I used one of those big Oxo tins for a money-box and, after a few weeks, I counted sevenpence ha'penny. Gran still wasn't happy about it especially when I told Peggy Haskins that I'd decided to put the price up and made her cry.

"They're bigger bundles now," I explained. "I'm not botherin' about the ha'penny trade no more. 'Tain't worth the trouble."

Peggy went and told her mother and very soon the news was all round the village. That horrible little Wilshire boy was asking a penny a bundle for patchwork. Chip off the old block he is. Like his granfer.

I didn't care what they said. I had tenpence ha'penny in the tin and was set to make a fortune from patchwork. When kids complained I said, "You want to buy it at a penny whilst you got the chance. I might put it up to twopence next week."

Every day I would count the contents of the tin and gloat over my big break-through. And then, one day, I went to the tin and found it empty.

"Somebody's pinched my patchwork money," I said. "There ought to have been one-and-tuppence but it's gone."

Gran blushed. Even as an old lady she still blushed.

"I pinched it," she said. "An old man, thin as a rake, came to the door and I hadn't a penny by me. He didn't ask for money but anything I could spare. Turned out he hadn't a bed for the night, nothin' to eat for days. So I gave him all your money. He couldn' hold back the tears. 'Bless your heart, missis,' he said, 'you've saved a life today.' I had a tear meself, when he was gone."

"Yes," I thought. "With my money." And, for a moment, I was on the point of telling her she was hopeless; that she'd always be poor; and then I thought of Granfer. What would he have done? Well, the old chap would have been sent packing with a flea in his ear. I'd still have my one-and-tupppence intact but it was worth that to see my gran so happy... He might have been a scrounger but, there again, he might not.

"Did I do wrong?" she asked ."I'll pay it back when I gets paid for this dress."

"No," I said, "you did right, Gran. It must've been worth it to see his face."

"It was," she said, beaming. "Worth every penny."

Next time a little girl came for patchwork Gran nodded towards me "You'll have to see our Lewis," she said.

The little girl proffered a penny but I said, "No, I've decided not to charge. Patchwork's free."

Gran smiled to herself as she stitched. She was happy. We were going to give it away. It would be nice to see the childrens' faces when we told them.

I looked at her and then I looked at the empty tin and suddenly I felt older than she and wiser.

"Do you realise, Gran," I said, "that if we hadn't charged for patchwork you wouldn' have been able to give that old man the money?"

"Yes," I said, "we'll go back to giving 'em patchwork. But only one bundle each. That's fair."

CASUALTIES OF TIME:

On the left: I am leaning against a fallen apple tree in Granfer's orchard, undermined by a wayward badger.

Above right: some years later, after Granfer's death, the orchard has become a putting green where my brother-in-law, my father and I enjoy a quiet afternoon game. A few years after that, the trees, the putting green and the cottage were all swept away to make room for what is now known as Gorse Hill.

Below: Charnell Wood which has entirely disappeared beneath concrete and housing, now merely a district of Mangotsfield.

The Collector

SOME PEOPLE ARE BORN SECRETIVE. **My Granfer Wilshire was. He saved his thoughts like he saved other things, too. We knew where he kept them, some of them.**

We never threw away a bottle and there was a pile of them dating back to his childhood in a cupboard in the outhouse. His money would be under the stone floors or up in the roof. His "things" were out in the workshop in a tea-chest. It had an old sack over the top, carefully folded, so that he knew if anyone touched it.

Whilst he was alive, Granfer jealously guarded his secrets. He never allowed anybody into the back of the cottage or outhouse. It wasn't until he died, in 1947, that we were able to find out what it was all about. The bottles we threw away. Looking back, *that* wasn't very clever. They'd be worth quite a bit now. But we threw them away. Along with much else that, if we'd saved them, as he had, would be worth a mint of money.

It was the money that interested Gran, of course. He'd kept her short all their lives together. Now she was able to look in all his secret places. There were pennies up the chimney and shillings under the floor, florins in boxes and even some golden sovereigns in a leather bag.

But what interested me most was that tea-chest. It had been sitting out there, in the workshop, for most of his lifetime. It didn't contain money or deeds and yet he had made a mystery of it. Why?

"What d'you reckon's in there?" I asked Gran.

"Oh, just a lot of rubbish," she said. "'Tain't worth grubbin' about in there, my son. 'Tis just a few things he didn't want anybody to see."

If it wasn't money, Gran didn't want to know. Not that she was greedy, she only wanted to give it away but it was her opportunity to spread it around a bit.

On the other hand I wasn't so much interested in money as the mind of the man. Although I'd lived with them for years and knew my gran inside-out, as you might say, Granfer had always been a mystery. He was remote, unfriendly, suspicious. Of course I *spoke* to him but he had always been monosyllabic—a man without friends.

That's why I was interested in the tea-chest. Here, if anywhere, I would discover his secrets. I examined it carefully, lifted the sack and... It was a great disappointment. All I could see were hundreds of bits of leather. Not one of them was big enough to do a decent shoe repair even. I should have explained that Granfer had been a shoe-maker in his younger days before factory-made boots killed off his trade.

I sat down on the floor to sort out the decent bits and it was then I discovered that the leather was only a ruse. Half-way down the chest I came across some old newspapers and, on top of them, residing like eggs in a nest, were balls. Fifteen altogether. Mostly children's rubber balls with tennis balls, cricket balls, golf balls—even a deflated football. Along with them was a cheap mouth-organ which I recognised. That, and the cricket ball, were mine. Why had he taken and hidden them? Well, now I came to think about it, he had never liked the mouth-organ, blamed

Gran for buying it for me. The balls must have represented a threat to his apple crop.

For us, when we were young, the world could be roughly divided into two types of people: those who gave you your ball back when you'd thrown or hit it into their garden—and those who wouldn't.

Granfer was one of those who wouldn't.

He had nothing against sport so long as it was conducted somewhere else, but if it threatened his crops or boundaries it had to be stopped.

That explained the presence of so many balls. It also explained the presence of a sixpenny bat (from Woolworths) and a "compo" cricket ball. As soon as I saw it I remembered those games of cricket with an old, gnarled apple tree as a wicket. We used to play in the orchards when Granfer was out. We had thought he never knew and that the bat had been stolen by gipsies.

Next in the strata came a layer of newspapers. Not *whole* newspapers or front pages. They were always the pages my mother called *Hatched, Matched and Despatched*. And they dated from the 1920s. It was not difficult to understand why they were there. Granfer had ringed round the particular item that had interested him in indelible pencil. And his rings had a triumphant flourish—as if to say, "There's another of 'em gone. But *I'm* still *here*."

A wartime paper carried an obituary of his son, George. No indelible ring round that. The smudgy photograph looked unreal as though, when it had been taken, Uncle George was already a ghost.

I was deep down in the tea-chest now. Forty years had passed since he had hidden this toy drum, tin pistol and penknife. They must have related to a previous generation. I asked my dad if he remembered them.

He remembered them all right.

"They're all mine," he said rubbing his eyes in disbelief. "That drum was a Christmas present when I was a kid. I never had such a thing before—your granfer didn't agree with toys— and I kept tapping at it all day. By the end of the week the old man said he could hear it in his head even when I *wasn't* beating it. He carried on at me mother and she said boys would be boys and it disappeared.

"As for the pistol that was a present from your great-uncle Joe. With two boxes of caps. Made a beautiful bang when it went off. I fired it in Father's ear and woke him up from his afternoon nap. That disappeared, too. But the penknife, now, *that* was different."

"Why?" I asked. "Has that got a story?"

"Oh, ah. I bought he with money I'd earnt doing errands. And I'd bought'a for a purpose... I was going to kill our George."

"Not really *kill* him?"

"Oh, ah. I was very young, see, and I was fed up with always bein' the bad boy. George, he was always favourite. It was

'Why don't you eat up properly like your brother? Why don't you be a *good* boy like out little George?' I tell 'ee I got fed up to the teeth with George."

"What happened?"

"Well I crept up on him when he was asleep. I thought I'd say it was a burglar what done it but when I looked down at him with the moonlight on his face, looking so peaceful, I just couldn't do it. Just then I heard a foot on the stair and it was Father. I dropped the knife, jumped back into bed and pretended I was asleep. When I looked for the knife next day it had gone. I wonder if he guessed ... he never said anything."

There was not much left in the chest. Just a notebook that had slipped down the side and a child's petticoat with a lace frill. Father had never seen them before so I took them to Gran.

"Why, bless me soul," she said, taking the petticoat, "that was our poor little Sarah's. Fancy him keeping it all these years."

She took the dusty garment from me tenderly. Her eyes filled with tears.

"Silly man," she said, "silly, silly man."

I looked my question.

"She was our youngest. Came when we thought all that was behind us. Lovely little ways, she had, and he came as near to being a human as he ever did. But she couldn't abide him. Told him he was a migler to his face. Told'n he saved his money and neglected his love."

"What happened to her, Gran?"

"Never met a child like her. Never. Old for her years and... different. Somehow, different."

"What happened to her, Gran?"

"She was only five, never reached her sixth birthday. Doctor said it was something-or-other but I put it down to a fright."

"It was meningitis, Mother," Dad said.

She took no notice.

"She was always terrified of spiders and some naughty boys put a daddy-long-legs down her back. She just stood there and screamed. A shock like that can bring on anything. Come the end she *knew*. 'Now you're not to get upset, our mum,' she said, 'Let *him* do the crying, he's got more to cry about than you.'"

Dad said, "Right to the end she wouldn't let him near her. That really got to him, that did. Only time I ever see'd him cry."

And he had kept her petticoat. In the tea-chest. All those years.

Now all that remained was the notebook. It had coarse paper which had gone yellow. Full of figures—Granfer's savings—how much he'd got for some pigs, his apple crop, and how much he'd paid out for barley-meal and stocky-bands. Apart from that there were a few bare details. The dates on which his father and mother had died and little Sarah and when Uncle George was killed on the Western Front in 1917. All the dates when his children were born and when they married. In the year my father married, 1921, he had sold

four pigs and noted 'Glad to get rid of them' though it was not clear whether he meant Father or the pigs. After that there was only one entry apart from the figures.

1922. Lewis born June 22nd.

Alongside it was a cross.

I'd give ten pounds—and I'm not a wealthy man—to know just what that cross meant.

Granfer hated being photographed, so maybe it was by way of protest at being cajoled to stand in front of the camera that he decided to wear this "ancient and disreputable coat", as my Gran's described it!

The Door of Darkness

HOW CAN I BEGIN?

Well, it *has* to begin with me, because it happened to me. And I must explain, right at the start, that I'm not a religious man. I've read religion and philosophy, but, like Omar Khayyam, a favourite of mine when I was young, I ended up by coming out by the same door wherein I went.

Do you know that verse from *The Rubaiyat*?

Strange, is it not, that of the myriads who
Before us passed the Door of Darkness through,
Not one returns to tell us of the Road,
Which to discover we must travel too.

This is not quite true, of course. It certainly isn't true of me, because I've been through that door. At least, I *think* I have. Let me tell you about it...

I was in my forties, married, with two children (they're grown up now) and I had this fierce attack of 'flu. There is no doubt that I was very ill.

The doctor had been, and my wife was warned. Lying in bed, I had that feeling of weakness and weightlessness that come from fever. I did not want food, and could drink only water. Outside, the sun was shining: it was May. Inside the bedroom, I slept fitfully, and woke, and there was no clear division between waking and sleeping.

It was then, that afternoon, that I drifted into this strange state of wakefulness. Only I was not in my bedroom. I was one of a crowd, moving down a narrow road with high banks. My eyes and mind were unusually clear, yet I was puzzled...

Although I was one of a crowd, the others were presences. They did not walk, but drifted. They were faces—puzzled, anxious, looking for someone they knew, wanting reassurance. From this confusion I wanted to escape, so I moved out of the crowd, onto the grassy bank, to watch them and wonder. I can see it now... their faces were troubled, yet they did not see each other. All of them looked for a familiar face—a friend—and the crowd pressed on, down the road, without knowing why or where they were going.

Glancing over the top of the bank on which I was sitting, I saw a view. It was as clear and bright as a miniature painting. 15th century. Smooth, enamelled fields sloped down to a river which reflected the sunlight and sparkled as though it was itself a river of light.

A few miles up the valley was a town, turreted, with walls round it, like a mediaeval Italian city. I saw the sunlight on its turreted towers, and I saw a long black line of beings stretching from the road below me down to the town itself, like an army of ants. Where it reached the city, there was an entrance-gate around which was confusion. Some wanted to get in, some were struggling to get out. It was puzzling.

Whilst I sat there, wondering what it was all about, an old man, leaning on a stick, climbed up on the bank from the meadows. He was more real than the thronging crowd in the road, and he stood beside me, watching them.

"Where do they think they're going?" I asked.

"They don't know."

"Why do they stare about them, as though they are looking for somebody?"

"They're expecting to be met," he said drily. "They haven't got over the shock of being dead."

"Are they all dead?" I asked.

"They wouldn't be here if they weren't. Most of them are shocked to know that it's happened to them, and that there are other existences than living. They're looking for a relation or friend."

"That," I said, "is why they're so anxious? There's no reception committee? They're on their own?"

"Some of them," he remarked, "have never been alone before. It's a terrible burden for them to be separate like this."

"And where are they going?"

"To the city," he said, pointing with his stick at the turreted town below.

No reception committee...

"Some of them don't seem to like it when they get there," I said. "Are they being turned away, or something?"

"No, no," he said. "Nobody's being turned away. It's just that it isn't what they expected." He looked down at me, and the faintest of smiles crossed his face. "When they find there's no sport, sex, food or television, they want to leave," he said. "They haven't accepted the fact that their five senses are dead."

"Can they go anywhere else?"

"No," he said quietly, "there's nowhere else. They'll wander about a while and then fade away, except of course," more cheerfully, "those who do accept."

"Accept what?"

"That they're no longer people but spirits; that all the things they lived for are gone for ever; that they are pure thought and that they're in a different dimension."

"But this bank," I said, "these flowers"—I've always been a

keen botanist, loved flowers for their beauty and originality—
"they're real enough."

"Touch them," he said.

I reached out to touch them. There was nothing there.

It was then that I realised something else. Although I heard
him, he had never actually spoken. His lips didn't move. He
must have known what I was thinking, for he said:

"Touch me."

I reached out to touch him, but there was nothing to touch.

Because I was confounded, he said, "You see—it's a
projection of your imagination. You can create anything you
like, but it won't be real. At least, not in the sense you think of
as reality."

"But that city," I said, "the fields, trees, river—it can't all be
imagination."

He nodded.

"Is nothing real?" I asked.

"It's real if you see it," he said. "You see a city, fields, flowers
because you want to. Everything has to come from within. If
there's nothing inside, then there's nothing to survive. If you
can accept that, you can go on. This isn't the only city—there
are many, all different. You might travel to thousands before
you find what you want, but they are all cities of the spirit and
they are peopled by spirits—like me."

"Who are you?"

"My name is William."

"What do you do here?"

"I look after the sheep."

"I don't see any..."

"No, you wouldn't, but I do."

I was about to ask him how he kept sheep if he lacked touch,
sight and bearing, when the dream—if it *was* a dream—ended
abruptly.

"It's time for your tablets, dear," my wife was saying, from a great distance, and I was back in the bedroom, feverish and weak, seeing her blurred shape bending over me, only half-conscious.

"I've been dreaming," I said.

She laughed.

"It must have been a short dream," she said. "I haven't been out of the room more than two minutes, and you were awake then. At any rate, your eyes were open."

That was fifty years ago, and I've never had a dream like it since. Perhaps it wasn't a dream at all. Maybe I had stepped through that Door, for a moment, and returned.

There's only one way to find out.

Secret Underground Bristol (2nd revised edition)
By Sally Watson

This is the second, revised edition of the most popular book ever written about Bristol, first published by the Bristol Junior Chamber in 1990, and back by popular demand. **Secret Underground Bristol** is a voyage of discovery into the world beneath your feet: mysterious tunnels, caves, nuclear bunkers, forgotten mines and underground waterways. This beautiful new edition has been substantially extended and brought up to date, with new information, access details, fascinating photographs and specially commissioned maps.

£14.95 • pbk • 128 pages • colour illustrated throughout • ISBN 1 874092 95 8

The Street Names of Bristol (2nd revised edition)
By Veronica Smith

Following the tremendous popularity of the first edition, published in 2001, we are delighted to present an extensively revised second edition, containing the new researches of the author, historical photographs, a new map of Bristol and the mountain of new information generously supplied by the Bristol public. Here are the origins and meanings of Bristol's districts as well as the thousands of streets within the Bristol city boundaries, in a book teeming with the historical and topographical detail of kings, philanthropists, healers, saints and murderers, builders, paupers, politicians, millionaires, and landscapes long forgotten but for their echo in the names of Bristol's streets.

An invaluable resource book, to which further contributions are warmly invited, and a wonderful read for anyone interested in their city's past.

£11.95 • pbk • 320 pages • 25 b/w photographs • ISBN 1 874092 90 7

Go Home and Do the Washing!
Three Centuries of Pioneering Bristol Women
By Lorna Brierley and Helen Reid

"The educated woman is the hinge upon which society turns" declared Hannah More in 1790, explaining her mission to educate and house the poverty stricken girls and women of Bristol. Hannah is one of the more famous philanthropic women that Bristol and its non-conformist tradition has produced, but here are detailed the lives of scores of unsung heroines: doctors, educators, housing reformers, suffragettes, writers, singers, explorers and artists, many of them given their just recognition at last.

£9.95 • pbk • 166 pages • b/w illustrations throughout • ISBN 1 874092 91 5